abc's
of
Electronic
Organs

by NORMAN H. CROWHURST

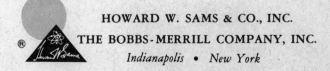

HOWARD W. SAMS & CO., INC.

THE BOBBS-MERRILL COMPANY, INC.

Indianapolis • *New York*

PREFACE

Today the electronic organ is one of the most popular home entertainment devices. There are well over a million organs in use and sales are on the increase each year. Electronic organs may be found in schools, theaters, and churches, as well as in the home.

The advent of the transistor has brought about many changes in electronic organ design. Effects which could not be considered previously, because of limited space and cost, can now be included at a price that is within reach of the average person. For the budget-minded, there are organs which are even less expensive than before, and which produce music that is more acceptable than from comparably priced organs of a few years ago.

Many people consider an electronic organ as being extremely complex. Actually, the circuits in a modern organ are no more complicated than those which you would find in a television receiver, radio, or audio amplifier. Because the range and versatility of an electronic organ requires that simple circuits be duplicated many times, the instrument appears more involved than it really is.

This book is exactly what its title implies—a simple explanation of all aspects of electronic organs. It begins with music fundamentals and progresses through the history and development of the pipe, reed, and modern transistorized electronic organ. The book tells you what an organ is, what it can do, how it works, how to play it, how to keep it working, and what to keep in mind when you purchase an organ. There is also a chapter for organ tuners—professional or amateur—dealing with various organ-tuning techniques.

Through the use of many tables, diagrams, pictures, and photographs, the electronic organ is explained inside and out. Many important terms which are needed by the prospective organ buyer may be found in the glossary.

Whether the reader is an avid music lover, organ owner, prospective buyer, or technician, this book will serve as a guide to understanding this fascinating musical instrument.

NORMAN H. CROWHURST

CONTENTS

CHAPTER 1

CHAPTER 2

CHAPTER 3

CHAPTER 4

CHAPTER 5

DEVELOPMENT OF THE ELECTRONIC ORGAN

In view of the apparent complexity of any modern organ, electronic or otherwise, it may come as somewhat of a surprise to learn that the organ is probably the oldest of those musical instruments that bear a resemblance to their original form. The word "organ" is derived from the Greek *organos* meaning "system." The organ, then, is a machine for playing a large number of separate instruments in succession or at the same time systematically.

Before the techniques of producing musical sounds in an organ are discussed, a look into the fundamentals of music will be helpful.

NATURE OF MUSIC

In the music of the Western hemisphere, all sounds except some percussive effects (drums, cymbals, etc.) are based on the twelve-note octave scale. Each frequency represents a note, but these notes must be properly related to one another in frequency. Achieving this relationship is called tuning. Western hearing (as opposed to Oriental; European is also considered Western in this sense) is accustomed to sounds in this particular relationship as being musical. Both melody and harmony depend on these tone intervals. In melody it is the relationship between one note and the next one played that produces the effect.

Octaves and Keys

All notes represent the same musical tone spacing from one to the next. This spacing, or interval, is about 6% of the frequency of the lower note of a pair. Twelve notes (including both white and black on an organ or piano keyboard) make up an octave. This means that two notes, spaced 12 intervals apart, have frequencies in a ratio of exactly two to one. In other words, the upper note has exactly twice the frequency of the lower.

Thus, starting with a certain note, you could pick out a melody by counting notes up and down in succession. Provided you got the right numbers for each step, it would not matter with which note you started. As long as the count were right, it would sound like the same tune, only set in a higher or lower "key." This is due to the uniform musical spacing of the frequencies for all notes.

A long time ago, the Western scale was diatonic. In other words, the interval was not uniform, but followed a special pattern. Changing the key, or the main note around which a tune or melody was built, changed its sound because the intervals would be slightly different, causing a "flat" or "sharp" effect. The modern equal-interval scale—called even, or equal, temperament—makes it immaterial in what key music is played, and also simplifies the design of electronic organs in some respects.

Chords

Where several notes are played at once instead of in succession, the effect is called a chord, or harmony. Just as note intervals in harmony can sound right or wrong in producing a tune, using the right combination of notes in a chord can also result in harmony or dischord. Different groups of tone intervals, when played together in a chord, make different harmony effects, to which musical names have been given (Fig. 1-1).

The octave, or 12-interval spacing between notes, produces a unique effect because the frequencies are in a ratio of exactly two to one, as mentioned earlier. When other pairs of notes are played together, some degree of harmony or dischord is noticeable because of the interaction between the two notes. Each interval or group of intervals, called a chord, produces its own characteristic effect. But two notes an octave apart, played together, sound like the same note. For this reason, they have been given the same name, or letter.

The scale of white notes runs C, D, E, F, G, A, B, and then C an octave higher. The black notes between C, D, and E, and between F, G, A, and B are called flats or sharps—after the note to their right or left, respectively. But all notes, whether black or white, are successively at equal intervals; so between C, D, and E, and between F, G, A, and B (where there are black notes) the intervals are twice as great as between B and C and between E and F.

It is these harmony effects, along with the melody, that can give music a bright, melancholy, or "blues" mood. However, music—to sound "solid"—needs bass. Every chord has a "master" note to which the group of notes seems to belong. Playing the same basic group of notes in a different order (Fig. 1-2) does not alter the master note, or key, to which the chord belongs. It is this note, played in a low octave, that makes the whole effect sound right and solid when added as bass. A note in the octave below the

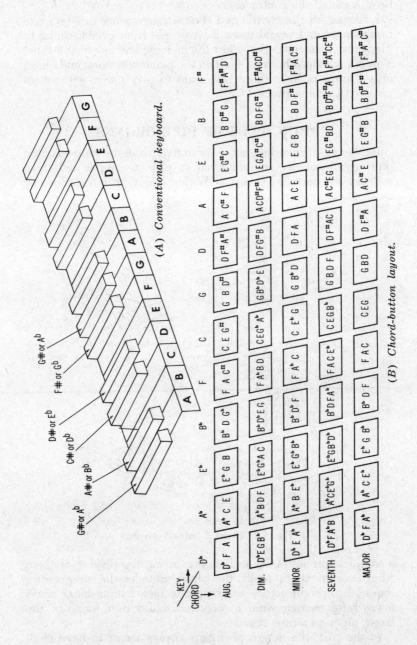

(A) *Conventional keyboard.*

(B) *Chord-button layout.*

Fig. 1-1. Typical keys and buttons.

9

master note of the chord, but played on the alternate or "second" beat, is called the contra bass.

Learning all the chords and their arrangements can be quite complicated and would deter most people from ever learning to play music—except perhaps just the melody, one finger at a time! This is why chord buttons, both on the piano accordion and chord organ, are a boon to those who want to play music without an involved learning process.

PRINCIPLES OF PIPE ORGANS

Replacing the earlier, more primitive wind instruments, the pipe organ enables an individual to play a complicated tune, melody, and harmony that would otherwise require the efforts of

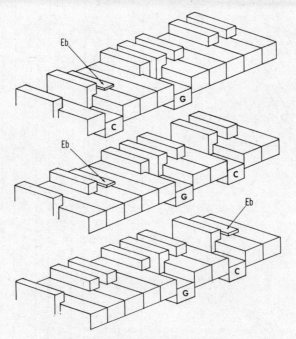

Fig. 1-2. Three *C* minor chords.

a complete orchestra. As well as organizing the playing of these wind instruments or pipes, the organ provides the air pressure required to produce their full range. In fact, human lungs could never raise enough wind to produce sound from some of the larger pipes on a pipe organ.

In the past, the design of organs always seems to have challenged man's ingenuity. Before the discovery of electronics, pipes

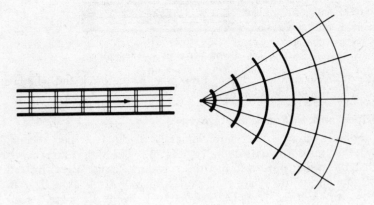

(A) *In a pipe.*   (B) *Outside the pipe.*

Fig. 1-3. Sound waves.

of all kinds, shapes, and sizes were devised as a means for exploring the possibilities of organ music. Long, thin ones and short, fat ones—although perhaps producing the same note—may lend an entirely different quality to the tone. Making the pipes of wood or metal also changes the tone quality, since the pitch of a note is determined by the frequency of its vibrations.

"Surely a note having the same musical pitch will have the same frequency of vibration, whatever instrument produces the note?" you may ask.

This is quite true, but vibrations are often produced at more than one frequency at a time. In pipe instruments like the organ, the vibrations coming out of the voice aperture of the pipe contain more than one frequency. The arrangement of frequencies de-

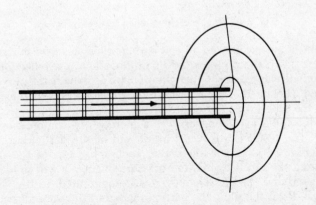

Fig. 1-4. Wave released from open pipe.

Fig. 1-5. Sound wave in stopped pipe.

pends on the shape and size of the pipe, its material, and whether its opposite end is open or closed.

Pipes and Sound-Wave Motion

Sound waves travel approximately 1,100 feet per second, whether inside or outside an organ pipe. The only difference is that the organ pipe restrains the traveling sound wave, instead of allowing it to radiate freely and dissipate itself as it does in open air (Fig. 1-3). As the wave travels inside the pipe, its intensity is virtually undiminished until it reaches the far end. What happens then depends on whether the end of the pipe is open or closed.

If the end is open, the sound wave suddenly finds itself unrestricted and its air particles suddenly move much more freely (Fig. 1-4). If the end of the pipe is closed, the sound wave cannot travel any further, and the motion of the air particles suddenly ceases (Fig. 1-5). Either way, the normal travel of the wave

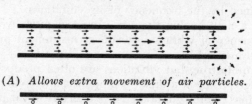

(A) Allows extra movement of air particles.

(B) Starts rarefaction wave down the pipe.

Fig. 1-6. Wave reaching open end of pipe.

through the pipe comes to an end and another wave starts traveling back down the pipe toward its origin. Each is a reflection of the original wave, except that the manner in which the wave is reflected (hence the effect produced) depends on whether the end of the pipe is open or closed.

Assume the wave going up was a momentary compression of the air. The result is a forward movement of the particles in the wave (Fig. 1-6). When this wave reaches the top of the pipe (assuming the top is open), the pressure of the air will suddenly be released and the particle movement exaggerated; in the wave reflected down the pipe, the particles move in the same direction as the arriving wave (opposite the direction of the return wave).

12

(A) Pressure increases.

(B) Pressure wave starts back.

Fig. 1-7. Sound wave reaches stopped end.

So the latter is a rarefaction wave, or one of reduced pressure, rather than a compression wave like the one that came up.

If the top of the pipe is plugged ("stopped"), the pressure will increase when the wave hits the end. As a result, a wave of the same kind (a pressure wave) will start back down the pipe (Fig. 1-7).

Frequency of Pipes

Now let's consider frequency in relation to the travel of the sound wave inside the pipe. Suppose a pressure wave starts up the pipe, hits the stopped end, and returns to the starting point in the same amount of time as half a vibration of the originating frequency. The downward motion of the air (due to the wave re-

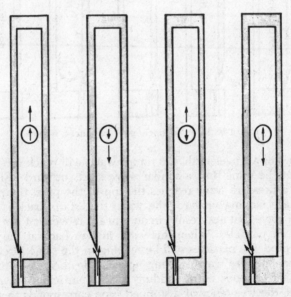

Fig. 1-8. How a stopped pipe produces a tone.

flected from the top of the pipe) will arrive just as the second half of the wave starts its downward motion (Fig. 1-8). The two effects will augment each other and build up an oscillation of the air at this particular frequency.

This effect is shown in the illustration, where the circled arrows represent momentary particle movement and the attached arrows indicate wave motion. Conditions at four intervals in a complete tone period are shown. The frequency will be such that the return journey up the pipe and back is half the wavelength. In other words, the length of the pipe is a quarter of a wavelength.

If the end of the pipe is open, the excess movement will start a downward-moving reverse wave. Assuming the length of the

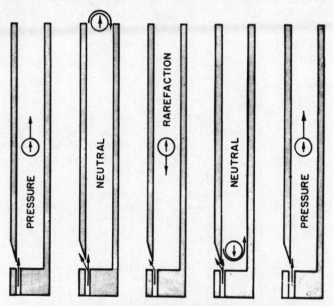

Fig. 1-9. How an open pipe produces a tone.

pipe is half a wavelength, the return wave will reach the starting point at the same time a similar wave starts upward (Fig. 1-9). When a pressure wave reaches the top of the pipe, the particles of air are moving upward; the wave that starts back is a rarefaction wave, but also results in an upward movement of the individual air particles. When this wave arrives back at the bottom of the pipe, the particles will be moving in the same direction as the next pressure wave starting upward. So this wave, too, augments a frequency corresponding to this particular wavelength.

Thus, the frequency of a stopped pipe corresponds to a wavelength four times the length of the pipe; the frequency of an open pipe corresponds to a wavelength twice the length. In other words, each lower octave doubles the length of pipe.

A rank of 12 pipes covers an octave of notes ranging from one C to the B above. Since C has the longest pipe, the whole rank is designated by C. Thus, the naming of a rank of pipes by their length denotes in which octave their notes will play.

This custom has become so firmly established in organ building that ranks of notes played in certain keys when a particular tab, or stop, is pulled are identified by a footage figure—even though the organ uses reeds or electronic generators instead. For exam-

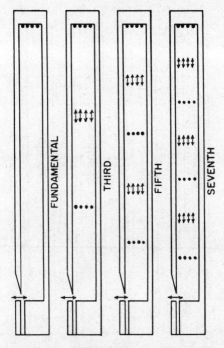

Fig. 1-10. Possible modes of vibration in a
stopped pipe.

ple, if the C at the bottom of the scale plays at a frequency of 32.5 vibrations per second ,the tab will be marked $16'$.

The other frequencies a pipe can produce depend on whether the wave coming down the pipe (the return wave) arrives in time to augment another wave starting upward. In the stopped pipe, the time for the wave to go up and back must be equivalent to half a period of a vibration, one and a half periods, two and a half periods, or any multiple of odd half periods (Fig. 1-10). In the illustration, the dots represent points where pressure fluctuations

15

due to combined arriving and returning waves reach maximum; the double-ended arrows indicate points where particle movement reaches a maximum. In the open pipe, an exact multiple of periods for the arrival-and-return time, or half-periods for the single-direction journey, will result in a frequency the pipe can produce (Fig. 1-11).

Harmonic Generation

In practice, a pipe may produce all possible frequencies at the same time when excited by wind being blown into it. If the pipe

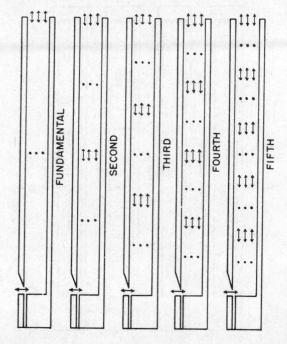

Fig. 1-11. Possible modes of vibration in an open pipe.

is much larger in diameter than in length, it will tend to produce the fundamental frequency. Conversely, if the pipe is relatively small in diameter, it will tend to produce the higher frequencies and in greater intensity. Expressed musically, the harmonic structure is said to be richer in the second example.

If the pipe is stopped at one end, the frequencies it produces will all be odd multiples of the fundamental (lowest) frequency—3, 5, 7, etc., times. If the pipe is open at the top, the frequencies it produces will all be odd and even multiples of the original frequency—2, 3, 4, 5, 6, etc., times.

16

If the pipe had completely rigid walls or sides of, say, solid cast cement, the relationship of the overtones or harmonics would follow a uniform pattern. For example, each successive frequency might be half the intensity of the one below it, or some other regular arrangement. Since most pipes are made of wood or metal their walls can vibrate and so can the air traveling back and forth inside. As a result, some of the higher frequencies are emphasized, whereas others tend to be restricted. It is this property that gives pipes their characteristic "metallic" or "woody" sound.

This property of producing many different overtones to the main pitch, or fundamental frequency, is not unique to pipes. So do stringed instruments and other tone generators, for that matter. This is what made it possible for pipe-organ makers to produce wind-generated tones, with specially made pipes whose sound resembled that of violins and other stringed instruments. By careful proportioning of the pipes, it is possible to produce a pattern of overtone structure similar to that produced by the strings and structural features of the violin, viola, cello, and bass viol.

Keyboards

In the twelfth century, organs were played by pulling out or pushing in slides to control the air passing from the wind chest (pneumatic or hydraulic pumps) to certain pipes. There were also organs played by pedals or a combination of pedals and slides. The first keyboard of the type used today was built in 1361 and restored in 1495.

Early in the development of the organ, several types evolved, each with its own characteristic tone quality and range. These are now known as sectional organs and consist of the great, swell, choir, solo, echo, and pedal organs. Even though they may play the same note, each has its own identifying sound.

When pipes were added or two or more sectional organs combined to increase their range and versatility, additional keys and consequently keyboards were required. Each keyboard was played by hand and for that reason was called a manual.

One of the earliest organs with more than one manual was the gigantic one built at Winchester, England, in the tenth century. It had 400 bronze pipes, 26 bellows in the wind chests, and two manuals of 20 keys each controlling 10 pipes.

Today, organs with four manuals plus pedals are quite common, and some even have five manuals. The uppermost manual is usually called the solo. It takes the role of the singer or a solo instrument and is usually played with one finger at a time. Successively lower manuals can represent different groups of singers in a choir or different groups of musical instruments in an orchestra. These may be played in combinations on each manual or one at a time as on the solo manual, according to the kind of music being played. Stops or tabs, associated with each keyboard, enable the player to select the instrument or group of instruments to be imitated by the keyboard.

The term "stops" originated with wind-operated organs, where it was applied to certain knobs on the front of the console. The knobs were only handles that activated valves to admit wind to ranks of pipes. In true organ terminology, the stops are actually the ranks of pipes. Today, because of modern styling, the knobs are often called "tablets," or "tabs."

Many persons, looking at a large pipe organ in a church or large auditorium, think it must be an extremely difficult instrument to play. Certainly it is not easy to play like a concert organist. But if you ever have the opportunity to sit at the keyboard of one of these instruments, you will be surprised at how easy it is to make sounds that seem almost professional, especially if you can play a piano. With very little practice, you can make much more pleasing sounds with an organ than with a piano, even if you are not a professional.

Advantage of System

The great advantage of the organ is that it can produce tones of all different types, like the sections of an orchestra. One group of pipes may produce a series of tones similar to those of the violins, another group similar to those of the woodwinds, and still another group similar to those of brass instruments such as horns and trombones. The sounds of these instruments are provided by the way the mechanical couplers are arranged and by the use of separate keyboards (manuals). These sounds resemble those produced by sections of an orchestra when they play their individual parts.

STRINGED INSTRUMENTS

In stringed instruments (whether a violin, guitar, or other instrument where strings are manipulated with the fingers; or a piano), the string is the main vibrating medium that produces the sound. In every stringed instrument, however, a soundboard is required to radiate the sound of the vibrating string. In a violin the strings go over a bridge, which communicates the sound to the body of the instrument. The body, in turn, radiates the sound waves (Fig. 1-12). In a piano, the bridge over which one end of the string passes is mounted on the soundboard. It is the vibration of this soundboard that produces the radiated sound, rather than the vibrating string itself.

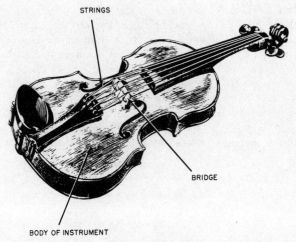

Fig. 1-12. Violin.

Electronic Piano

Electronic pianos have been built without a soundboard. Both terminations for the string are completely rigid, preventing any sound radiation except from the strings. Without some electronic or acoustic pickup close enough to the strings to amplify their sound (in the same way the soundboard of a normal piano does acoustically), such pianos can barely be heard, even in a noise-free room.

REED ORGANS

Early in this century, the reed organ became popular. It used vibrating reeds, similar to those of an accordion, instead of pipes, to generate tones. It, therefore, was more compact than the pipe

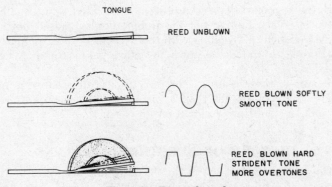

Fig. 1-13. Tone of reeds.

organ but could produce many of the effects. The simpler types had just one set of reeds and no stops; the more complicated had more than one set of reeds, with stops that enabled the reeds to be played in various combinations from the individual keys.

A more common feature was a series of stops. These adjusted the sound pressure (or vacuum) communicated from the main bellows chest to the manual voice box and thus varied the vibration of the reeds. Changing the intensity changed the pitch slightly. However, the quality was altered much more, because the sound of a reed is caused by the "bursts" of air admitted past

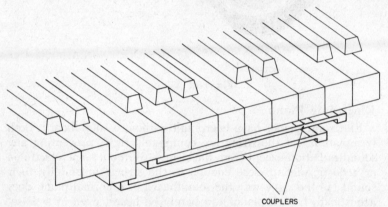

COUPLERS

Fig. 1-14. Coupler mechanism for keys.

its tongue. Blowing harder invariably makes the sound richer in overtones (Fig. 1-13).

Like their bigger brothers, the pipe organs, some of the reed organs had more than one manual of notes. Another feature of the bigger pipe organs and some reed organs was the coupler (Fig. 1-14). When one note was depressed, a mechanical device underneath the keyboard depressed other notes related to it, usually at octave intervals. Pulling out the treble coupler caused notes an octave higher to play, along with the depressed note. Similarly, a bass coupler sounded the notes an octave below the ones being played.

Because of these features, the reed organ can produce a much wider variety of sounds than a piano. In other words, it takes less skill to sound professional on an organ than on a piano.

HISTORY OF ELECTRONIC ORGANS

Prior to the appearance of the vacuum-tube amplifier in 1912, attempts at artificial production of musical sounds were necessarily limited to acoustical and electromechanical methods. These had one limitation—extremely complex mechanisms were required.

Soon after the tube amplifier had been developed, many electronic and electromechanical systems evolved. One of the first was an oscillator unit in which the frequency was controlled by the body capacitance of the operator. Called the *Theremin* (after its Russian inventor), it was played by moving the hand near a set of capacitive elements. Not long after the beat-frequency technique used in the *Theremin* was perfected, a keyboard was added. Recently there has been renewed interest in the instrument.

Early application of the vacuum tube to organs was primarily for amplification of the feeble signals developed by the electromechanical tone generators. One of the first electronic organs contained a set of tuning-fork oscillators with electromagnetic pickups. The forks vibrated and induced voltages into the coils, which developed signals that were amplified by vacuum tubes.

Photoelectric and optical tone generators were experimented with as early as 1922. In 1926 an organ was demonstrated that used an optical system consisting of perforated discs driven by a synchronous motor. As the discs rotated between a set of small lamps and a photocell, the varying signal from the cell was modified and amplified to produce the tones.

Photoelectric organs were produced in the United States by the Baldwin Organ Co., and in Germany by the Welte Organ Co. Optical representations of the desired waveforms were placed on a transparent disc which rotated between an exciter lamp and photoelectric cell. (There is a great similarity between this method and the optical sound-recording systems used in the motion-picture industry.)

The link between the purely mechanical and purely electronic tone generation appeared in the early 1930's with the development of tone-wheel and reed generators, which are still popular today. The tone wheel usually employs electromagnetic principles and the reed is electrostatic or capacitive (although there are also capacitive tone-wheel systems).

In the last ten years, great advances have been made in the development of electronic tone generators. Transistorized organs are quite common today, and many with advanced tube and electromechanical tone generators are on the market.

MODERN ELECTRONIC ORGANS

The latest adaptation, to make it even easier for persons without formal training to play an organ, is the addition of chord buttons to the organ. Actually, chord buttons are not new; they were derived from another wind instrument, the accordion.

Chord Organs

The earliest accordions had no keys, only buttons. Each button played only one reed—or two reeds, one when air was forced out of the bellows and the other when air was pulled in. The buttons were arranged in patterns at both ends of the instrument; and the player had to learn which buttons to press, and in what sequence. To make accordions easier to play, and also to enable them to produce more varied effects, the piano accordion was developed.

In the piano accordion, the right hand plays a keyboard similar to that on a piano or organ. The keyboard operates reeds, just as in the reed organ. The only difference is that they are mounted in one of the end assemblies, whereas on an organ they are mounted on the frame. At the opposite end of a piano accordion are chord

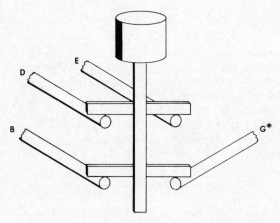

Fig. 1-15. Coupler mechanism of a chord organ.

buttons. Each button operates a group of reeds by means of an arrangement similar to the coupler on the keyboard of the reed organ (Fig. 1-15). Instead of coupling simply the octave notes, however, each button on the bass end couples together a group of reeds that play the required chord.

By using one finger at a time on his left hand and one on his right hand, the player of a piano accordion can achieve complete harmony and a full musical score. Of course, he can play chords with his right hand if he wishes, using several fingers at once. He can also play the chords with his left hand in rapid succession, achieving an effect that would be impossible without chord buttons.

So we see that the early mechanical changes, probably intended to make playing easier, have also made it possible to produce much more complicated effects. It was only natural that these developments would eventually be applied to organs, to produce what is now called the chord organ.

With the simpler chord organs, the melody is played with one finger of the right hand, on the keyboard to the right. Meanwhile the left hand, one finger at a time, selects the appropriate harmony on the chord buttons to the left. If the organ has bass pedals, they are played with the left foot to give the deep bass, while the *swell* (volume) is controlled with the right foot.

Regular Organs

Most electronic organs have two manuals plus a set of pedals, or a pedalboard. The upper manual is called the swell, or solo; and the lower manual the great, or accompaniment. Near the center of the pedalboard is a larger pedal, which is recessed into the cabinet of the organ and increases or decreases the volume. There are also sets of tabs or stop keys to control the tone quality of the various sections.

With a two-manual organ, more complicated effects can be achieved than are within the scope of the chord organ. The melody is played with one finger of the right hand on the upper manual; and the harmony is played with the left hand on the lower manual, using several fingers to select the notes of the desired chord. The tabs are selected to alter the tone quality of the melody and harmony; and switches can be adjusted to introduce special effects such as vibrato, tremolo, and percussion. Vibrato causes the melody (and harmony, if desired) to waver in pitch like a soprano's voice—whereas tremolo, a closely related effect, causes the volume to waver. Percussion makes the notes sound as if they were being struck sharply, as on a xylophone.

Organs are available with more or fewer of these features and with a wide variety of arrangements, to be discussed in later chapters.

In addition to the controls already mentioned, other external features of the typical organ (Fig. 1-16) include some like their counterparts on the piano. A music rack which folds down over the keys or back onto the top of the organ is standard on organs, as are keyblocks (end cover plates) between the ends of the keyboards and sides of the organ. The keyboards are quite similar to those on pianos, differing from organ in the shape and number of keys. There may also be a cover, called a fall front, that can be pulled down over the keyboard.

The stop keys and special-effects switches are mounted on a tone-color panel directly above the upper manual or to the sides of the keyboards. Each tab and switch is labeled with a simple description of the effect it produces. For example, a voice tab may

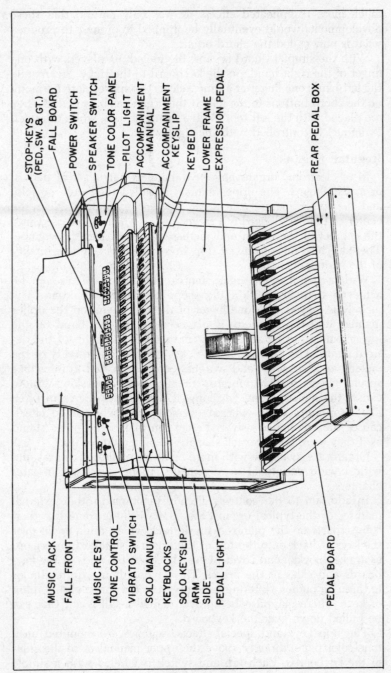

STOP-KEYS (PED., SW. & GT.)
FALL BOARD
POWER SWITCH
SPEAKER SWITCH
TONE COLOR PANEL
PILOT LIGHT
ACCOMPANIMENT MANUAL
ACCOMPANIMENT KEYSLIP
KEYBED
LOWER FRAME
EXPRESSION PEDAL
REAR PEDAL BOX

MUSIC RACK
FALL FRONT
MUSIC REST
TONE CONTROL
VIBRATO SWITCH
SOLO MANUAL
KEYBLOCKS
SOLO KEYSLIP
ARM
SIDE
PEDAL LIGHT
PEDAL BOARD

Fig. 1-16. Baldwin console Model 5.

be labeled Flute 4', Cello 8', or Viola 8'. Special-effects switches are labeled Tremolo Lo, Vibrato Med, Timbre Lo, etc.

Other controls in the same area are the power and speaker switches, tone control, etc. The pilot light is often located near the power switch. The labeling, shape, and location of the switches and voice tabs vary from model to model and from one

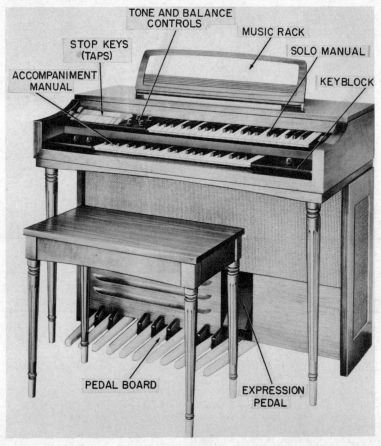

Fig. 1-17. The Thomas *Serenade* (Model VT-2).

manufacturer to another (Fig. 1-17), as do the number and placement of the pedals in the pedal board.

Organs are available in any wood finish and in a wide variety of period styling. Many accessories are offered, such as auxiliary speakers in cabinets with matching finishes.

CHAPTER 2

ELECTRONIC
SYNTHESIS OF SOUND

Modern electronic organs use one of three main forms of tone generators — mechanical-acoustical, electromechanical, or electronic.

MECHANICAL-ACOUSTICAL TONE GENERATORS

Mechanical-acoustical tone generators consist of a vibrating reed or string. Electronic amplification merely enlarges the acoustic output (Fig. 2-1). Although the tone quality can be changed during amplification, the basic sound is always that of the reed.

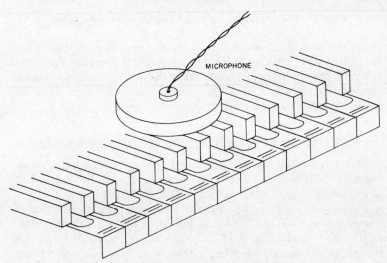

Fig. 2-1. A microphone mounted over reeds.

The reeds are so small that one microphone usually is able to pick up the sound of a whole bank.

Modified piano frames have been used, with electrical pickups placed close to the strings at carefully chosen points. Although the quality is basically that of the strings (which are usually steel), it can be modified quite extensively by careful placement of the pickups (Fig. 2-2). However, the sound is not that of a piano, despite the fact that piano strings are used.

A modified piano frame has no conventional soundboard to radiate the normal piano sound. Without amplification, the tones produced are so feeble that they are almost inaudible. Electronic amplification modifies the sound tremendously. Because the volume is adequate to sustain the tone acoustically, the sound is

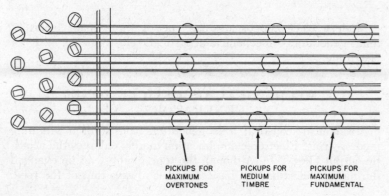

PICKUPS FOR MAXIMUM OVERTONES   PICKUPS FOR MEDIUM TIMBRE   PICKUPS FOR MAXIMUM FUNDAMENTAL

Fig. 2-2. Electrodes in an experimental electronic piano.

more like that of an organ than a piano, even though the strings are vibrated by striking them as in a piano. Changing the point at which the sound is picked up from the string, along its length, changes the overtone structure in ways quite different from the limited possibilities of electronic circuits alone.

ELECTROMECHANICAL TONE GENERATORS

In electromechanical systems, the tone is generated by mechanical motion. However, there is no vibration as such; the equivalent of vibrations is generated in electrical circuits.

There are two types of electromechanical tone generators in common usage today. The better known one is the rotating magnetic tone wheel (Fig. 2-3). A steel cam is rotated near a coil wound on a magnet, inducing a voltage in the coil. After being filtered and amplified, this voltage produces a note, the pitch of which is determined by the number of cam flats or teeth passing the coil each second.

Another type of electromechanical generator uses a fluctuating electrical capacitance in a tone-wheel system. One plate of a capacitance is etched on a cam, which is rotated close to a fixed plate. A detector circuit develops the voltage, which is shaped

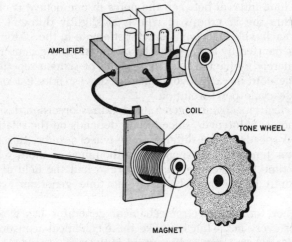

Fig. 2-3. Magnetic tone wheel.

into the note. This method, which is similar to the magnetic tone wheel in a mechanical arrangement, is rare today.

Other means have been experimented with using recorded sound tracks of the desired waveforms on similar tone wheels. The wheels are rotated at such a rate that the waveforms repeat with the desired frequency for each particular tone. Any recording system could be used in this way. Experiments with optical and magnetic systems have also been performed. The mechanical phonograph groove might also work, but would be rather clumsy.

With all electromechanical generators, at least 12 tone wheels or sets are needed, one for each note in a complete octave. The

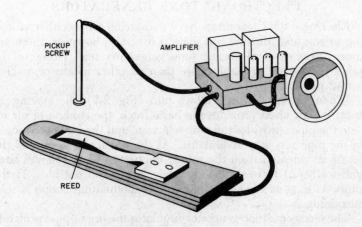

Fig. 2-4. Electromechanical-reed tone generator.

proper tone interval between the notes in one octave is obtained by driving the 12 groups of wheels at slightly different speeds, to give each wheel its own characteristic note in the 12-tone scale. Notes separated by octaves can be mounted on the same rotating shaft, merely by having two, four, eight, or sixteen repetitions of the same note in each revolution. The lowest note has only one complete cycle per revolution.

The electromechanical generator requires precision design and manufacture. Moreover, since tuning depends on the relative mechanical speeds of the different tone-wheel groups, this type of generator tends to be expensive (although it is more reliable). At one time the electromechanical organ had the field almost to itself, until the completely electronic tone generator was perfected.

Another form of electromechanical generator has a separate reed for every note—but is unlike the mechanical-acoustical reed generator, where the acoustic output of the reed is used. The reeds are mounted in a soundproof box, where a fan keeps them in vibration as long as the organ is switched on. Each reed acts as one plate of a capacitor, and an electrode just above it is the other plate (Fig. 2-4). The reeds and electrodes are in circuits that produce notes as the capacitance varies, similar to the system of capacitive tone wheels. The electrodes can be adjusted to tune each note to the right pitch. This system develops many harmonics as well as the fundamental movement of the reed, and its tone is more like that of a pipe organ than an acoustic-reed system.

Reeds can be used in both capacitive and magnetic or inductive circuits, but these systems are not popular today.

ELECTRONIC TONE GENERATORS

Electronic tone generators have no moving parts, either vibrating or rotating. Beyond this main distinction, however, there are more varieties of electronic tone generators than either of the other types—and probably more than all other means of making sound put together.

When an organ pipe is blown into (Fig. 2-5), the moving air from the air chest provides the basic force, the column of air inside the pipes provides the tone selection, and the air at the mouth of the pipe acts as a "modulator." As the pressure (1) behind the jet of air released from the nozzle fluctuates, the jet moves back and forth (2) to feed air alternately inside and outside (3) the pipe. As long as the air jet blows, this modulating action is self-sustaining.

The electronic tone generator simulates the organ-pipe principle electronically. The power-supply voltage of the electronic gener-

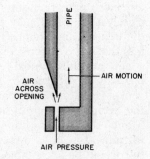

Fig. 2-5. Acoustic tone-sustaining
principle in an organ pipe.

ator is like the compressed air in the organ chest. Electrical components in the tone-generator circuit correspond to the pipe in selecting the tone or note, and an electronic modulator replaces the air-modulation effect at the mouth of the organ pipe (Fig. 2-6). The electronic modulator may be a vacuum or gas discharge tube, a transistor, or almost any other electronic device that will provide amplification.

Although the circuits that provide the tone colors can produce a wide variety of effects, these effects differ from the ones available from an acoustic organ. The mixture of tones and overtones that an organ pipe produces is due to the dimensions of the pipe, coupled with the timing of the sound waves inside the pipe. An organ pipe has natural overtones that are close to multiples of the lowest frequency—the note by which the pipe is recognized.

Unlike the air waves in pipes, the electrical quantities in electronic circuits "move" virtually instantaneously. The swelling of sound, which in pipes is due to the progressive build-up of waves traveling along them, must be achieved in other ways in the electronic tone generator. Electronic circuits produce sounds with different overtone content—usually by shaping the wave electronically rather than by selecting the frequencies going into it, their proportions, and the speed at which each builds up. That is why

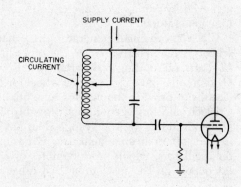

Fig. 2-6. An electronic
tone-sustaining circuit.

any electronic organ sounds different from a pipe organ, however closely the former may try to copy the sound. Because of this difference many organists, who have been trained on pipe organs, feel that the electronic organ does not produce music. This is not a new attitude. Probably every musical instrument, in its time, has had to struggle for acceptance among the "classical" musicians. There are still some professional musicians who maintain the saxophone is not a musical instrument, for a similar reason!

Such die-hard traditionalism is not at all logical. Every musical instrument is, in its own way, artificial. Only the human voice itself would be acceptable, if one went back far enough in this rejection of artificiality. This aspect is mentioned because it helps to decide an important question: "Should the electronic organ be regarded as a means of imitating other instruments, particularly the pipe organ, or should it be judged as a new kind of instrument in its own right?"

Some of the tones which electronic circuits could generate would not be judged as being musical—even to the most untrained listener. But the tones and sounds that come from an electronic organ do fit into the tonal pattern of modern music, and the organ can be played with other instruments when desired. This means the electronic organ has to be accepted as a musical instrument. Once it is, there is no reason why an electronic organ should be limited to imitating sounds made by other musical instruments. Its versatile design permits it to produce a variety of sounds unlike those of other musical instruments.

TONE RANGE

A pipe organ requires a pipe for every note played. (Most have hundreds or even thousands of pipes.) Each key can play any combination of pipes. Organs using mechanical-acoustical tone generators have at least one for each keyboard note—whether it be a reed, string, or some other kind. Different tone qualities are achieved by using electronic circuits, as well as additional sets of tone generators.

Electromechanical generators may have any number of tone wheels, which correspond to the pipes in a pipe organ. However, 12 shafts, all rotating at different speeds, will carry all tone wheels. Or there may be only one tone wheel for each note, and electronic circuits to provide the various tone qualities.

Electronic tone generators probably have more possible variations in filling the tone range than any of the other types. The most common arrangement uses 12 basic tone generators, or master oscillators, which produce notes of either the highest or lowest octave on the instrument. All other notes are then obtained

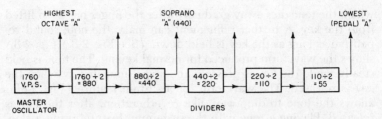

Fig. 2-7. Electronic divider system.

by electronic circuits that either multiply or divide the outputs of the basic tone generators successively by two to develop the octaves above or below (Fig. 2-7).

In an electronic organ with only 12 basic tone generators, or oscillators, they must function all the time, in order to be ready to produce notes in all octaves. To provide greater flexibility in the tone color, some organs have separate tone generators for every note on the keyboard. Each generator need not be oscillating all the time, but only when the appropriate key is pressed. This allows different effects to be produced by switching the tones on and off in different ways.

As an alternative, an organ in which the tone generators are functioning all the time has circuits that control the amplification of the tone generators as they are played, to produce similar percussive or sustained effects. Which way is better? This is difficult to answer. It depends on the individual organ. The best way to tell is by listening.

Changing the way the waveforms of the tones start and stop can produce sounds like chimes, or can add a sustained effect in

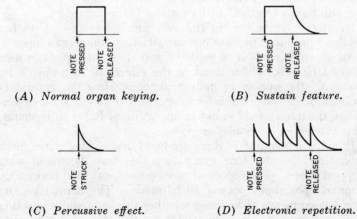

(A) Normal organ keying. (B) Sustain feature.

(C) Percussive effect. (D) Electronic repetition.

Fig. 2-8. Waveforms for the development of electronic percussion.

which the tone dies away gradually after the finger has been lifted from the key. A further refinement can make the note sound repetitive as long as the key is held down. (See Fig. 2-8.) Fig. 2-8A shows the waveform produced for normal keying. The tone is held steady while the key is pressed, and stops immediately when the key is released. The waveform for a sustain feature (Fig. 2-8B) allows the tone to die away, like reverberation, after the key is released. Playing a tone with the sustaining feature, using a staccato (striking) touch, produces the waveform in Fig. 2-8C. This results in a percussive effect. An electronic repeating oscillator will make the percussive effect, like that of a xylophone or marimba, as long as the key is held down (Fig. 2-8D).

SIMULATING INSTRUMENTS

How can an electronic organ simulate the different tones produced by musical instruments? There is a variety of methods. Some electromechanical tone generators actually use a separate tone wheel for every instrument represented. On that tone wheel is inscribed a waveform copied from the original instrument, or from a pipe-organ reproduction of it. This means the electronic organ reproduces the original sound exactly, like having separate recordings of each note produced by every instrument shown on the tabs. Needless to say, this is an expensive method.

Some organs mix together the needed overtones from the range of higher notes generated in the same organ. The next octave up is the first overtone (second harmonic). This is a perfect overtone. Then a tone interval of a major fifth above the upper octave is almost exactly three times the original. The second octave up is the third overtone (fourth harmonic), while the major third above that will be close to the fourth overtone (fifth harmonic).

Overtones synthesized in this way are not exact—but neither are those produced by most instruments, including organ pipes.

An alternate method of getting the desired tone qualities uses formant circuits, which simulate the effects of instruments by modifying the quality of individual tones. Here the generators produce tones very rich in harmonics or overtones. Without formants, the tones would sound rough or fuzzy. But with formants, all overtones or harmonics are exact.

In musical instruments there are two types of tone colors, both determined by the tone generator. This was illustrated with stopped or open pipes. Stopped pipes possess only odd harmonics, whereas open pipes possess all harmonics. The normal voicing filter has no means of knowing whether the harmonic it is acting on is odd or even. The only way to get this kind of difference is to start with a different form of pulse waveform.

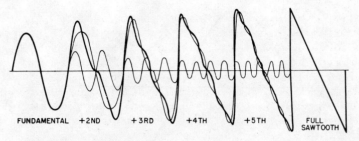

FUNDAMENTAL +2ND +3RD +4TH +5TH FULL SAWTOOTH

Fig. 2-9. Development of a sawtooth wave.

Most pulse waveforms used in organs are sawtooth (Fig. 2-9). Since they have all the harmonics of the fundamental frequency, they cannot readily imitate the effect of a stopped pipe and certain woodwind sounds. For this purpose, a symmetrical pulse waveform is needed.

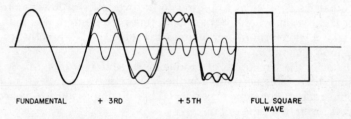

FUNDAMENTAL + 3RD +5TH FULL SQUARE WAVE

Fig. 2-10. Development of a square wave.

The square wave (Fig. 2-10) is ideal. It can be generated right at the tone generator with the sawtooth, so that the form needed can be used for each voice. An approximate square wave can be made by adding together two sawtooth waves an octave apart (Fig. 2-11). This is the method used in the Kinsman organ. The basic tone is changed to give it a hollow effect, throughout the scale, characteristic of the intended type of instrument.

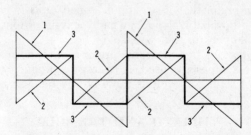

Fig. 2-11. Deriving a square wave from two sawtooth waves.

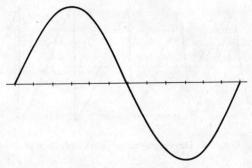

Fig. 2-12. Sine wave.

Extensive filtering can strip most of the harmonics from a pulse-type waveform, but must be designed to serve the whole range of tones. Otherwise, it will interfere with the relative magnitudes of the remaining fundamentals, because the higher notes will have frequencies equivalent to harmonics or overtones of lower notes. For this reason, where deep, smooth tones are desired, it is better to take a waveform nearer a sine wave (Fig. 2-12) directly from the tone generator.

None of these methods of producing the different tone qualities sound alike. This accounts for the "synthetic" sound of an electronic organ to someone experienced in listening to musical instruments, even to a pipe organ.

Although the tone given each admittedly is different, each is definitely musical. Choice is largely a matter of taste. Some argue that one is better than another. If "perfect" overtones are what we "should" have, then organs employing formants or a multiplicity of individual tone wheels are the only acceptable types. This would rule out other musical instruments as unacceptable!

In practice, once we get away from idealizing something that is really a matter of taste (like color, smell, and other subjective evaluations), the simple fact is that individual choice depends considerably on conditioning—what you are accustomed to. So if you have an organ that is accurately tuned (this *is* important), your taste will probably "adopt" whatever form of tone synthesis that organ happens to use.

An advantage of the electronic organ is that, no matter what type of tone synthesis is used, it is easy to produce completely new kinds of sound, as well as those of any familiar musical instrument.

VIBRATO AND TREMOLO

In music, the word *vibrato* means a warbling of the pitch of a tone, as produced by rocking the finger on a violin string; the word *tremolo* is applied to an intensity variation, as produced by putting a rhythmic jerk into the bellows' pressure of an accordion. The effects are really quite similar. In fact they are never completely isolated from each other.

In the reed organ, a revolving shutter in the path of the outgoing sound, usually controlled by the tab labeled "Vox Humana," achieves a satisfactory tremolo effect.

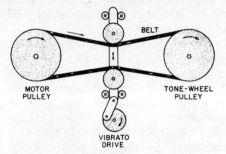

Fig. 2-13. A mechanical method of producing vibrato.

For a vibrator effect in the electromechanical type of organ, a variable-speed drive is introduced, either by using an eccentric pulley or by wobbling a drive belt (Fig. 2-13). In purely electronic organs, the most common method is to apply an alternating voltage to a circuit, to fluctuate the tuning of all tone generators and thus warble their pitch (Fig. 2-14).

PERCUSSION AND SUSTAIN EFFECTS

The electronic organ has an advantage in percussion and sustain effects. Earlier organs were provided with mechanically operated percussion—real xylophones, etc.—which was electrically controlled and could be amplified by a microphone. Percussion sounds are the most difficult to pick up and amplify with fidelity. So, although a real xylophone may have been installed in an organ, the amplified sound did not seem real.

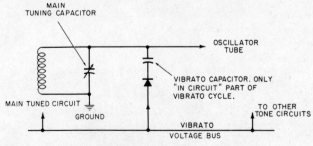

Fig. 2-14. Electronic vibrato circuit.

Electronically produced percussion may be no nearer a realistic imitation of the sound in the intended instrument, but it is a more pleasing sound to most ears—it sounds less "canned." The methods employed are essentially a simplified version of the work done by RCA with its "music synthesizer." First, RCA analyzed percussion sounds—their frequency content, rate of growth and decay, and any frequency shift during the whole period. Then tone generators were set up, with independent controls for each. In this way individual sounds could be simulated, both percussion and others, and new sounds explored as well.

A sudden sharp start, with a quick dying away (decay) at first, followed by a much slower dying away, sounds like a plucked string. If the decay is made more gradual, the sound is like that of a piano. With a changed overtone structure, the sound resembles that of a marimba or xylophone. Another mixture gives an effect like bells or chimes, and so on.

The addition of a simple low-frequency oscillator—to represent the rate at which a xylophone might be played repetitively—enables the tones to be "struck" at any desired rate. This is done by merely holding the organ key down, after the correct tab has been selected to bring this low-frequency oscillator into the circuit.

The possibilities for various effects are almost infinite. Of interest—but scarcely within the true category of an organ—is the Wurlitzer "Side Man." This electronic instrument uses the same general method to simulate drums and other percussion—such as cymbals, brush, wood blocks, etc.—in any desired rhythm. Instead of tones, it uses tube (or transistor) noise with formant circuits to get the "tone" of a brush, cymbals, etc. The timing circuits control not only the beat, but also the envelope, or intensity variation, during each beat. The effect is almost unbelievably realistic, and the "Side Man's" sense of rhythm is perfect! Electronic music, other than strictly organ, is only in its infancy and much more interesting effects can be expected as time goes on.

CHAPTER 3

FUNDAMENTALS OF ELECTRONIC ORGANS

All electronic organs look more or less alike and produce the same characteristic musical sound. This similarity may lead the layman to conclude that their interiors also are alike. Or he may notice that some organs have buttons whereas others have tabs, and still others knobs—thinking that these are only superficial exterior differences, like the choice between push button or lever in the automatic transmission of an automobile. Actually, the external controls and their arrangement do indicate the range and versatility of the organ—but not the mechanical and electronic systems used. Within the organ are power supplies, amplifiers, speakers, oscillators, waveshaping circuits, special-effects sections, mechanical linkages, and hundreds of feet of interconnecting wires!

WAVE GENERATION AND SHAPING SECTIONS

All organs use one of the systems of tone generation mentioned in Chapter 2. Where there is a separate generator for each note (C, $C\sharp$, D, $D\sharp$, E, F, $F\sharp$, G, $G\sharp$, A, $A\sharp$, and B), the generators can be grouped into 12 sets. Tone systems may also have 12 master oscillators with dividers, or several keys may take turns sharing one oscillator (Fig. 3-1).

Frequency Distribution

In addition to the tone generators, means must be provided for modifying the sound of the notes to imitate various orchestral sounds and to provide swell effects (increasing and decreasing loudness).

Many modern organs can provide tremolo, vibrato, sustain, and percussion effects. Each can be developed by a variety of methods. Many different tonal effects can be achieved by synthesis—mixing together the frequencies needed to obtain the desired note (Fig. 3-2). Tone quality may also be altered by a system called, in contrast, analysis (formant). In this system the tone is not actually analyzed, but is produced through a subtractive process.

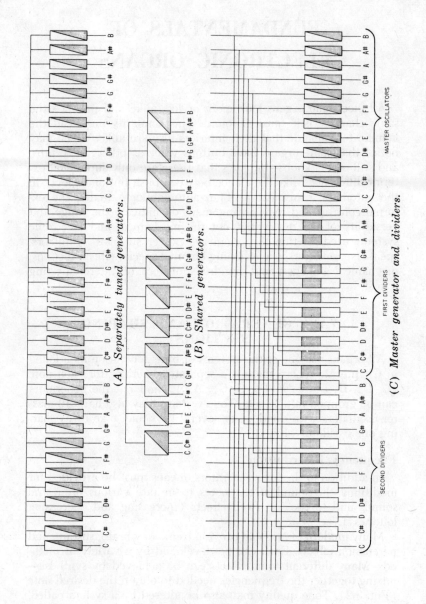

Fig. 3-1. Tone-generation systems.

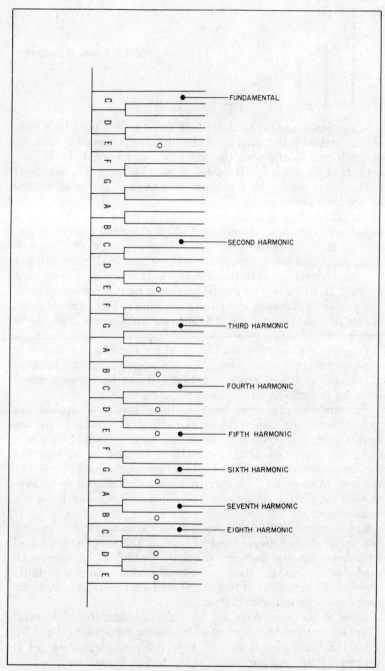

Fig. 3-2. Synthesis method.

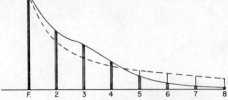

Fig. 3-3. Formant method.

In synthesis, the organ starts with more or less pure tone generation and adds the other individual frequencies needed to make up each note, along with the tonal quality required. Each note consists of the same fundamental-to-overtone ratio. The synthesis method is preferred by the Hammond Organ Co. for all organs except their chord organ.

The alternate and much more common process begins with a signal very rich in overtones, and alters the tonal quality by removing the harmonics (Fig. 3-3). However, none of the overtones are taken away completely. These modified tones are not the same harmonics of different notes, as they are in the synthesis method. In addition, every note developed by the formant process has a slightly different mixture of overtones. The over-all tonal effects produced by the two methods may, therefore, differ quite widely.

Whether synthesis or analysis is better for tone forming is a much-argued question. Some idealists prefer synthesis because of the realism it can achieve. Actually, it can be "more perfect" than the instrument whose sounds it copies.

To show the difference between these two basic approaches more clearly, the two ways of simulating a flute-like tone are shown (Fig. 3-4), with little harmonic—actually only a little second (first overtone). With the synthesis method, every note has the same composition. With only one formant filter (Fig. 3-4A) the level of successively higher frequencies is reduced. With synthesis (Fig. 3-4B) all notes are of the same level and harmonic composition.

The formant method, to give it the same composition, requires extremely sharp low-pass cut-off, unless the tone is generated with low-harmonic content, naturally (which is the approach used by generators that approximate sine waveform fairly closely). This makes the higher notes of lower intensity than the lower ones—an unnatural effect.

Some organs overcome this by using a succession of formant filters for sections of the organ rather than a single one (Fig. 3-5). Thus the fundamental can be kept fairly unattenuated, while progressive attenuation occurs at the higher harmonics in all octaves. The response shown at A is used for two octaves, the others

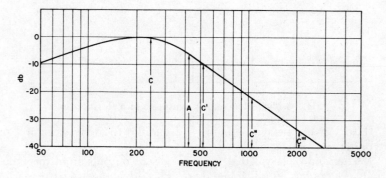

(A) Formant method.

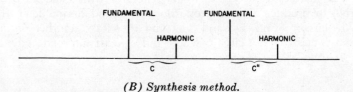

(B) Synthesis method.

Fig. 3-4. A flute tone by formant and synthesis methods.

each for one octave. These responses are typical of the flute formant responses used in Wurlitzer and other organs.

The clarinet frequency-selective formant must use a more "edgy" waveform to work on than is desirable for the flute tones. Then it must emphasize the harmonic structure, particularly the

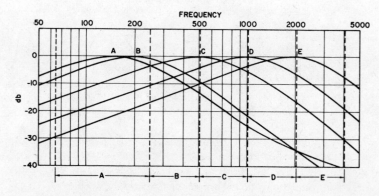

Fig. 3-5. Some organs use different formants for various organ sections.

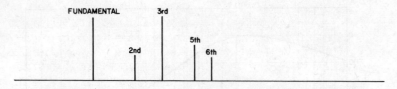

Fig. 3-6. Typical harmonic synthesis of a clarinet tone.

third. Again, the synthesis method enables the tone structure to be more consistent (Fig. 3-6).

The kind of organ that has two sets of outputs from the tone generators has an advantage here. This advantage is particularly applicable to organs that have individual tone generators, rather than a master system, and is exemplified in the Conn organ line. The oscillators use a tuned-circuit generator with sufficient overdrive to produce a good proportion of second harmonic in the main circuit (Figs. 5-7 and 5-8) and then take another output from a point in the circuit, where pulses exist more strongly, to derive the "richer" or reedlike tones.

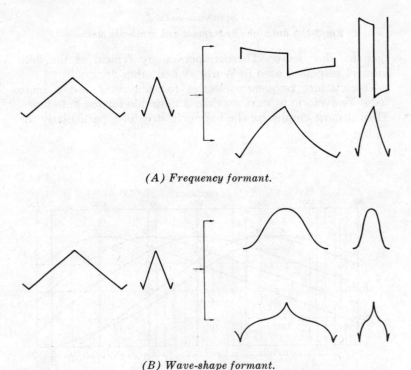

(A) Frequency formant.

(B) Wave-shape formant.

Fig. 3-7. Frequency and wave-shape formants with the same input waveform of different frequencies.

More modern organs also employ wave-shaping formants, as well as, or in place of, the frequency-selective variety. This distinction is clarified (Fig. 3-7). The wave-shaping variety operates on the wave, regardless of frequency, and thus is more like the synthesis approach. The top shows a signal through R-C networks with the capacitor in series and shunt respectively. The bottom shows a signal through waveshaping networks that round or spike the wave, respectively. The two are often used together in the same organ in recent designs.

In the simplest organs—with only one keyboard, or manual—a single set of tone generators is adequate. But when there are

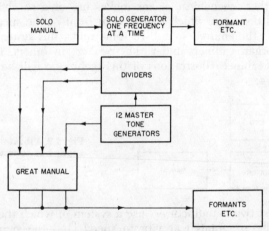

Fig. 3-8. One solo (swell) generator and separate accompaniment (great) generators.

two manuals, each should have a separate set of tone generators to increase the versatility of the organ.

In some of the early organs, the solo (swell) manual had only one tone generator and, therefore, can play only one note at a time. The accompaniment (great) manual has a set of tone generators (Fig. 3-8), allowing each note to be sounded independently.

In many organs, the same method is also used for the bass section, so that only one note at a time can be played with the pedals.

SPECIAL EFFECTS SECTIONS

Tremolo and vibrato may be produced by one of several means which fall into two main groups—mechanical and electronic. Percussion and sustain effects must be developed electronically. Additional effects such as stereophonic-like sound require the use of external auxiliary speakers.

The addition of such special effects raises the price of the organ, but their advantages are almost always worth the extra cost.

Tremolo and Vibrato

There are several mechanical methods of introducing the wobble in the sound for tremolo and vibrato effects. In one system used with mechanical generators, the speed of the motor driving the tone wheels is varied. A second method introduces a fluctuation into the belt or pulley drive to the tone wheels. In some electronic organs, a motor-driven variable capacitor in a phase-shift network develops a signal that modulates the master oscillator.

The other mechanical means makes use of a revolving baffle or sound deflector, which is placed in front of the speaker cone to warble the emitted sound. In some units, this system appears in the organ cabinet, under the speaker; in others, it is in a separate cabinet. Illustrations of this technique will be found in Chapter 4.

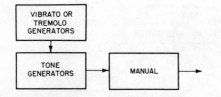

Fig. 3-9. Vibrato or tremolo applied to tone generators.

At least two manufacturers use a system in which the speakers and baffle are rotated at vibrato speed, and the signal to the speakers is coupled through brushes and slip rings.

There are also several electronic methods of producing these effects; all consist of low-frequency oscillators and each uses a different coupling system. The method of coupling the output of the vibrato oscillator to the master oscillator depends on how the latter is driven. In some organs, this is done by a low-frequency phase-shift vibrato oscillator and switch tube. If conditions permit, the vibrato generator may be coupled directly to the master oscillator, without intermediate stages (Fig. 3-9).

Another system used in many organs involves a vibrato oscillator and a vibrato amplifier (Fig. 3-10), which feed the diode section of the master-oscillator tube with the vibrato signal. One

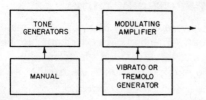

Fig. 3-10. Vibrato or tremolo applied to separate modulating amplifier.

other system consists of a phase-shift oscillator feeding a keying voltage regulator, which in turn drives the tone generator. These methods may all be used in transistorized equipment with the equivalent transistor circuits.

In each method mentioned, the tone generators are modulated to warble the tones as they are developed. The warbling effect may also be introduced at a later stage of the organ sound system, such as the lower-level stages of the audio amplifiers. The fluctuations may then be in the form of level variations or of changes in the frequency relationships.

Percussion and Sustain

Percussion and sustain can also be applied to the tone generators directly, or to amplifier stages after tone formation. However, while vibrato and tremolo can be applied to one amplifier stage for the entire organ (or at least one whole manual), every note requires a separate percussion signal, although the same circuit may supply them all (Fig. 3-11).

Sustain circuits, which are closely associated with the percussion sections, cause the note to die out slowly, thereby making it possible to create various chime and bell effects.

The gating technology of using diodes as switches has increased potential in this area. Didoes can be used in a keying circuit (Fig. 3-12) that can be used either for straight playing or for sustain and percussive effects. The waveform at the input is essentially of square-wave form. Before a note is depressed, the bias supply maintains diodes D1 and D2 nonconducting and D3 conducting, thus providing essentially infinite attenuation to the note.

When the note is depressed without sustain, the keying introduces offsetting positive bias, so that diodes D1 and D2 become conducting and diode D3 is nonconducting, to pass the signal. To achieve sustain, all that is needed is a capacitor from the keying point input to ground, so that the keying voltage dies away gradually, instead of abruptly, when the key is lifted.

As the diode bias changes it chops off part of the square wave, leaving part of a square wave as the voltage dies away (Fig.

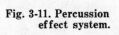

Fig. 3-11. Percussion effect system.

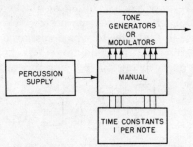

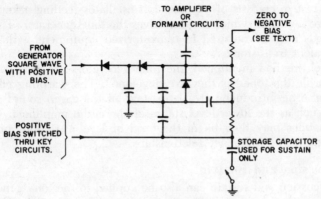

Fig. 3-12. One form of gating circuit using diodes for sustain as well as straight keying.

3-13). The bypass capacitors (C1 and C2) restore some rounding to the corners of the wave, so it does not sound "strangulated", which would be the effect of this changing bias without such reshaping.

The time constant of the sustain can be changed either by altering the value of the storage capacitor or by altering the voltage on the zero-to-negative bias circuit. A bigger voltage causes the signal to die away faster and with a more definite cut-off, resembling plucking or pizzicato. A smaller voltage allows the voltage to die away more slowly and less abruptly, more closely resembling a steel guitar effect.

Percussion

Those effects which produce sustain to tones that otherwise stop abruptly when the key is lifted are called percussion by many organ makers. When the effect was first added it did lend transient quality of a sort. But the initial sound when the key is depressed does not differ from a regular nonpercussive note. What makes a true percussive sound?

True percussive sounds are those of drums, cymbal, brush, etc. And the percussive sound of plucked strings, hammer struck marimba, etc., can be synthesized by adding elements similar to these to the notes to which sustain has been added.

Drums and other nontonal effects need keying in rhythm with the music being played. For this purpose, pulses can be derived

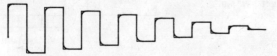

Fig. 3-13. The sustain waveform output from circuit of Fig. 3-12.

from the bass (pedal) note keying, to operate a bass drum, from the accompaniment (great) manual for snare drum operation, and from the solo (swell) section for cymbal and brush effects.

Additionally, a foot plunger or toe piston can be used to operate the cymbal or other percussive effects independently, so they can be clashed or boomed at the player's command only, or in addition to the musical rhythm requirements. How this is set up is a matter of control circuitry.

Drum sounds use resonant circuits shock-excited into near oscillation. They are much like a tone generator, except that the coupling is insufficient to maintain oscillation. The resonant frequency produces a sound corresponding to the pitch of the drum from bass to bongo.

Brush and cymbal require a hissing sound, for which a noise generator is used. This may be an open-circuit high-gain amplifier carefully shielded so that it does not pick up hum. Then the sound of the noise is controlled by gating circuits, just like the keying with diodes. Simple gating, with various growth and decay rates, can simulate ways of using a brush.

To get the effect of a cymbal, the noise signal, which is limited to about a two-octave range by series and shunt capacitors, is modulated by a "shimmer" oscillator as well as by the keying current (Fig. 3-14). The cymbal sound is keyed by a negative-

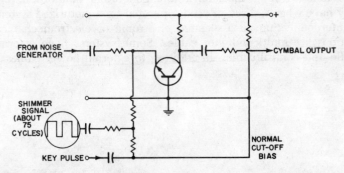

Fig. 3-14. A modulating circuit for synthesizing symbol effects.

going pulse from the key circuit along with negative-going pulses from the shimmer generator at about 75 cycles.

The percussive or strike effects, added to notes of the musical scale with sustain applied, give liveliness or attack; different manufacturers give various names to special circuits that do more or less the same thing.

A further addition to the same basic technique produces chimes. These are synthesized from four notes that use diode gating (or other variety) with sustain, and an additional strike sound electronically added. The diode synthesizing part is quite simple and typically plays the two octaves with the intermediate fifth and sub-third. Thus the frequencies played together are in the approximate ratio: 5/8, 1, 3/2 and 2. The simple diode synthesizing arrangement (Fig. 3-15) enables the switching to be kept simple.

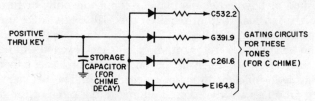

Fig. 3-15. Synthesizing each chime tone with diodes.

MECHANICAL LINKAGE AND CABLES

Most of the mechanical linkage is, of course, found in the keyboard and pedal areas, where its function is to throw switch contacts. These contacts may be to the rear of the keys, or in another part of the organ and connected to the keys by a set of control rods.

As mentioned, some organs use a form of mechanical vibrato or tremolo in which there are gears, pulleys, belts, shafts, or rotors. The same is true for mechanical tone generators; in addition, they may have wheels, discs, or reeds operated by a motorized system.

Interconnecting all associated electronic or electromechanical sections are multiconductor cables. Some systems have external audio and control cables, in addition to external power cables.

CHAPTER 4

MODERN ORGAN MECHANICS

To many people, the simplicity with which the effects can be achieved on an organ, and the degree of versatility in playing, are more important than the range of sounds possible and their degree of realism. The former are determined by the more "mechanical" features of the organ—arrangement of manuals, pedals and/or chord buttons, etc. In this area, too, there is variety enough to please everybody.

EXTERNAL ARRANGEMENTS

The professional organist will often dislike chord buttons and other "simplifying" features and demand an orthodox keyboard arrangement. An instrument with both chord buttons and normal features, however, can be played by many persons who have varying degrees of musical knowledge.

Chord Systems

For people with virtually no musical training, one of the chord organs may prove less complicated. But even it may not seem easy enough, because there is the problem of finding the right chord buttons without searching for every bar of the music. One aid is the little colored caps provided on some organs (Fig. 4-1); when placed over the chord buttons that produce a particular tune, the caps make the buttons easier to see and feel.

Another approach, adopted by Electro-Voice (Fig. 4-2), uses no chord buttons. Instead, 17 keys at the bass end of the keyboard have a dual function—they can be played in the regular way or, at the throw of a switch, will operate 17 of the most-used chords.

Transposition—To the novice, 17 chords sounds like a pretty good selection. Actually it is. Let's see what you do get—major chords for all the white notes, C through B, for B♭, which is eight out of twelve, and minor chords for B, F, A, F♯, D, C, and E, plus augmented A and G. These are enough to play quite a variety of music, especially if transposed in key to find a combination of chords that suit the needs of the piece.

All music can be transposed from one key to another, but there are seven fairly simple transpositions. These are reversible—making a total of fourteen—that are made visually by reading the music almost as it is written. In fact, four of the pairs—involving music set with from two to five sharps and the same number of flats—are made merely by reading enough of the opposite to make up seven.

For example, music set in three sharps can be played equally well by reading it as four flats. Every note is merely played one

Fig. 4-1. Chord-button caps.

semitone (one note) lower, and the music read exactly as written otherwise. Other keys may involve reading B for C, or E for F, or both, as shown in Table 4-1.

Incidentals—notes marked with additional flats or sharps to the ones indicated as the key in which the music is set—complicate transposition a little. For example, suppose the music is set in three sharps and you are playing it in four flats. If an incidental D♯ is indicated in the music, D would be played as D♭, so D♯ is played as D natural.

Similarly, suppose an incidental C natural is indicated. In three sharps, it would normally be sharp, but in four flats it would be

Table 4-1. Table of musical transposition.

Key	Number of Flats or Sharps	Key	Number of Flats or Sharps	Additional Transposition
C	Open	C♯	5♯	B-C, E-F
D	2♯	D♭	5♭	None
E	4♯	E♭	3♭	None
F	1♭	F♯	5♯	E-F
G	1♯	G♭	5♭	C-B
A	3♯	A♭	4♭	None
B	5♯	B♭	2♭	None

played as a natural anyway; so in transposition, it would be played as a *B*.

Suppose you want to play *Prelude in C♯ Minor*. You could do so by transposing—playing the music as *C* minor, in open key, and playing *B* for *C* and *E* for *F*—which is not as difficult to do as it may sound. The Electro-Voice organ has *C* minor as a chord, but not *C♯* minor. However, the *Prelude* is frequently published in *C* minor instead of *C♯* minor, to make it easier to read.

Fig. 4-2. An Electro-Voice bass section.

Many people who have had a limited number of music lessons find it easier to play music set in sharps than in flats, or vice versa. Hence, they will transpose anything in more than one flat or sharp into its opposite number if not written in the key to which they are accustomed.

This is why it is possible to get by with a lot of music by using only 17 chord keys. But much music cannot be completely accommodated, however it is transposed. For this, you flip the switch and play the chord directly, in the conventional manner as set forth in the music.

This is somewhat like the situation with a toy piano. The smallest come with an octave of eight notes (white notes only). Quite a few of the simpler melodies can be played—enough to give a child some pleasure. But a piece with any incidental sharps or flats cannot be played. The next improvement, with five black notes, gives a 13-note octave. On this any melody within an octave range can be played. The next improvement gives four extra notes above upper C, to E, accommodating several of the melodies just beyond the octave range. Still, there is much music whose melody could not even be played on a 17-note piano.

The same goes for chords. The 17 prechosen in the Electro-Voice organ cover quite a range, but there are many more that only a complete set could really cover. However, by reverting to the individual note action of the keys, these 17 notes can be played in various combinations for every chord.

Admittedly, where the music is simple enough to be accompanied by certain of the 17 chosen chords, it will be easier to find the appropriate keys than to find the right buttons in a chord-button panel. You have to learn which keys to use, but the special Electro-Voice music makes this easy. As the instruction manual states, you can make good music that way and graduate to playing the "proper" way, with a fairly easy transition—more easily than from the chord-button panel for most people. This is one example of the simplifications provided by organ manufacturers.

Hammond organs use quite a different approach. They recognize two difficulties for the beginner in much modern music. One is "finding" the appropriate bass notes with your left foot; the other is beating out a rhythm with the chord buttons. The job of doing both at once means that even a chord organ takes a little practice.

The Hammond chord organ (Fig. 4-3) provides only two bass pedals, which are coupled to the chord-button panel so they play the two "acceptable" bass notes (commonly known as bass and counterbass) appropriate to each chord. Alternate playing of the two pedals, or a regular beat on one of them, will always give the correct bass.

To aid in hitting the correct buttons with the fingers of the left hand, a rhythm bar (located in front of the button panel) can be played with either the left thumb or the wrist, allowing the correct buttons to be pressed more steadily. This means the finger movement can be much more leisurely—the wanted chords can be picked out, while the thumb or wrist controls the beat given by the selected chords. It's surprisingly easy to do.

No matter which chord organ you have, the chord section can do only so much. It is satisfactory as long as the right combination of notes is played for a particular chord. But some music calls for

Fig. 4-3. Playing the Hammond chord organ.

a rolling chord, in which the same sequence of notes is played in succession all the way up the keyboard; or a crossover chord, in which the notes of the chord are played an octave higher, instead of lower, than the melody; or a variation of the same chord, in which successive beats change the sequence of the note grouping or chord. None of these can be done with chord buttons or equivalent features.

Combination and Two-Manual Systems

For maximum flexibility, along with the simplicity that chord buttons or a similar arrangement can provide, you need the full organ facilities—either combined with or in addition to the chord arrangement (Fig. 4-4).

Some of the pedal basses are electrically connected so that only one bass note can play at a time. This is done both as an economy and as a quality measure—less electronics are necessary in order

Fig. 4-4. Wurlitzer two-manual organ with chord buttons.

for this section to use its own separate oscillator and to make playing much of the music easier. With a full bass section, if your foot accidentally touches two pedals, both will sound, causing a dischord. But with the addition of this feature, the dischord is avoided. In fact, you can actually rest your heel (or toe) on one bass pedal and beat another one with your toe (or heel). In this way, the two notes will sound alternately without a break and without your having to "feel" your way about the pedals.

Occasionally you may want to play two bass notes at the same time, for a deep-throated effect. This can be done only with an organ that can play bass notes independently.

The same is true of the upper, swell, or solo manual. In some organs the playing of a melody is simplified by designing the keyboard so only one note at a time can sound. If two notes are pressed at once, only one will sound—either the upper or lower—according to the design of the instrument. This can be fine for the beginner on some kinds of music—any lack of precision in fingering the keys can be covered up nicely.

But if you get used to playing an organ in which the lower of two notes sounds when pressed, and then play one in which the upper one sounds, your playing will be more upset by the change than it would by playing a regular organ in which any note pressed plays, regardless of whether others are pressed at the same time. If you plan to play only your own organ, these features may be fine. If you plan to learn to play any organ and to have anyone else play yours, however, regular keyboard operation is better.

The one-note-at-a-time feature is not as much of a drawback as you might expect. Practically all organ music calls for the solo part to be played one note at a time, to give the melody, while the other hand plays the harmony, either with chord buttons or chord combinations of keys on the great or accompaniment manual. If you have an accompaniment manual as well as chord buttons and the solo manual, the one-note-at-a-time feature on the solo is not a drawback. Moreover, it makes playing the solo part much easier for some people.

Some organs use electronic circuitry similar to that for vibrato to produce a gliding tone, or glissando, characteristic of a Hawaiian guitar. When such a circuit is used, it is almost essential to have some means to limit playing to one note at a time. Otherwise, some weird and unwanted effects could happen, like the playing of one note causing another already being played to warble. So here is another good reason why a one-note-at-a-time feature should be incorporated.

INTERNAL SYSTEMS

To the inexperienced ear, all organs sound alike. But to experts, some are unacceptable because of their sounds. There are considerable differences in tone quality. The reason the inexperienced ear finds these differences hard to detect is that all but the cheapest organs have quite a range of tone qualities, or voices.

Any moderately priced organ can simulate a range of tone qualities, from a full-bodied sound similar to that of a church organ to the lighter tone colors more usually associated with concert organs. The differences of quality between one organ and another are a little more subtle than this more obvious tone range. They seem to "come through" the various colors superimposed on the basic tones by the voicing of the organ. It is a difference in the basic tone quality that shows up when you become used to the organ, whatever stops you may use.

Reed Generators

One group of inexpensive organs, which is intended for home use and includes chord-organ features, is simply a reed organ with built-in microphones and amplifier. Most professional organists reject its sound, because reeds develop quite a different set of harmonics from any other tone generator. To the trained ear, they lack purity of tone—not that they are out of tune, but the tone quality doesn't sound right.

On the other hand, these organs have one advantage over any other home organ in the same cost bracket—they produce a fuller, richer sound because every note has its own individual tone generator, a separate reed. On most inexpensive organs, two notes played an octave apart will sound like one note—because that, in effect, is what they are.

Pressing the second key of the octave interval sounds just like changing the setting of the tabs rather than adding another note. With a reed organ, separate notes always sound like separate notes. Playing an additional octave, or using the coupler on a reed organ, adds much more "body" to the tone than it does on most electronic organs.

As against this advantage, the tone quality is much like that of a piano accordion. In many kinds of music, the sound of an accordion never seems to "fit." It is often regarded as a solo instrument for this reason, although it can be played in certain combinations quite effectively. Of course, if your organ is in your home, you may never intend to play it with any other instrument. So this aspect of the characteristic reed organ tone quality may not bother you.

Electronic Generators

In most of the purely electronic organs, and in the less expensive of the electromechanical variety like the original Hammonds (not their chord organs), the tone generators are rigidly locked together. The electronic ones have oscillators running at each note in the top octave of the instrument's range and every other note, right down to the pedal bass, is produced by successive frequency halving from this top octave. So the organ really only has 12 notes.

From these 12 notes, you can change the volume and tone color in a tremendous variety of ways by using the tabs and different octaves; but just 12 notes remain. If three different notes are played in a chord—say C, E, and G, with one on the solo (swell) manual, all three on the great (accompaniment manual), and the key tone, C, on the pedals—the sound will still resemble three notes being played, because it is drawn from just three of the twelve tone generators.

When you listen to a choir, the whole group may be singing each of the four parts—bass, tenor, alto, and soprano. Between them all, only four notes are being sung at one instant. But the choir has much more "body" to it than a quartet, in which each person takes one of the four notes. The reason is that, in a choir each of the four notes is being sung by more than one person in "unison."

The word "unison" is quoted because all choir members are never in perfect unison. This is why the group produces the effect of extra body rather than just extra loudness. The latter would be the effect with perfect unison, because there would just be "more voice." This expanded body is what most electronic organs lack. No matter how much the swell is opened or how many octaves are coupled in or played at once, the sound is that of a quartet, or one voice per note.

The big advantage of the locked-generator type is its simplicity and reliability of tuning. Only one octave of 12 notes need be tuned on one keyboard; the whole organ will then be in tune. Tuning or retuning—where the pitch needs changing for some reason—a whole organ, note by note, can be an almost impossible task; but reducing it to just 12 notes makes the job relatively easy.

Solo Type—An even simpler organ is the "solo" type. This is simply a small extra keyboard that can be fixed to the front of a piano. Its simplicity springs from the fact that it can play only one note at a time. If two notes are pressed at once, only one will sound (usually the higher note). This solo-organ addition to a piano is not to be confused with the piano organ at the end of the chapter.

Although the solo organ has few parts, it requires as much tuning as a full-sized organ. Every note must be adjusted separately and in the correct order, which usually differs from the ordinary tuning procedure.

Individual Generator—The opposite extreme from the solo organ is the one where every key on the organ controls a separate tone generator. This type merely reverses the advantages and disadvantages of the others.

Every tone generator on the organ must be separately tuned. The fact that different oscillators are used with direct control from the keyboard to switch the oscillators themselves rather than just the amplifier stages, means that this organ, when correctly tuned, has a fullness of sound the others cannot achieve. It also has a better range of tone colors, or voices, because each tone generator can provide several basic output waveforms, which the divider-type circuit cannot readily do.

Shared Generator—Besides the organ that has a tone generator for every note, there is also a compromise variety that provides some of the advantages of an oscillator for every key, but with considerably fewer oscillators and hence less cost. In some sections of the instrument, one oscillator serves for two adjacent notes on the keyboard. Very seldom are two adjacent keys played at once. In the rare event that they are, only one will sound.

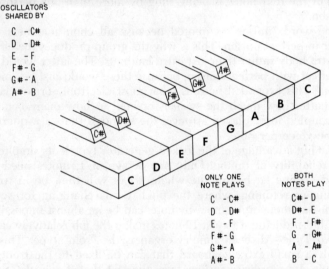

Fig. 4-5. Shared-oscillator combinations.

This failure of both keys to play occurs only if the two happen to share the same oscillator. If they share adjacent oscillators, both notes will play together (Fig. 4-5). So this limitation proves to be much less noticeable or objectionable than would appear from the first explanation of how the organ works.

The solo principle—only one oscillator for the whole section—is used in the bass region (the pedal organ) not only in this type of organ, but also in some with separate tone generators in the rest of the organ. Since it is unusual to play more than one note in the pedal register, a separate tone generator can be employed to get an exclusive-sounding bass tone. The only thing such a bass-pedal section cannot do is produce double bass tones, such as imitations of aircraft sound (made by pressing two adjacent pedals) or the deep guttural sound of bass chords, usually two notes a perfect fifth apart.

Tone Coloration

Now that we have considered the basic tone generators, our next question is the variation of voices and tone colors. These are quite similar except for the simulating of percussion effects. What many organs call a percussion effect is merely a "sustain" feature —a circuit that starts the tone the instant a key is pressed, and retains the note at uniform intensity (unless the swell or volume pedal is operated) as long as the key is held down. When the key is released, the note dies away gradually instead of at once.

To achieve a percussive effect with this kind of organ, not only must the sustain tabs in the control section of the organ be selected, but the keys must be played with a staccato touch (only tapped momentarily). The normal organ touch is a smooth one, in which one group of notes is not released until the next group is depressed—quite unlike the touch required to play a piano. On the other hand, the percussion effect on the organ requires an even more abrupt touch than normal piano playing does.

Some organs achieve the percussion effect more fully by coupling, with certain voicing circuits, a change to the keying circuit. In this way, the tone starts to die away immediately after it has been played, even with the key held down. This method enables some voices played by the same manual to be percussive and others to be a continuous, organ-type tone. The keys are played in the conventional organ manner.

An extension to this, achieved in the Thomas organs, is an "automatic percussion" system that repeats the strike, at a rate under the organist's control, as long as a key is held down. This enables xylophone or marimba effects and strumming to be achieved without repeatedly striking the keys. The organ is played in its regular manner, and the electronic xylophonist does the rest.

Most of the tone colors, or voices, are achieved by electronic filters which produce pulse-type waveforms rich in harmonics. This is where radical differences in basic tone can come through. Different tone generators produce basically different pulse shapes. The filters do not take the pulse waveform of each note and change its shape; instead, they take the whole manual output and change the relative distribution of the frequencies. Thus the fifth harmonic of, say, one tone may be weakened, while the same harmonic of another note in the same chord or melody may be strengthened.

This mode of coloration is similar to that produced by typical musical instruments. If the individual tone coloration of all notes is not good because of the poor pulse waveform; the *average* tone waveform will still get through, no matter what the voicing filters do. As a result, the quality will not sound as rich or good as that of another organ.

Vibrato is achieved by a variety of methods. Where a mechanical-acoustical generator is used, the only possible form of vibrato is electronic, incorporated into the amplifier, because the reeds or other acoustical generators cannot possibly fluctuate their pitch. A tremolo effect could be achieved mechanically by using a rotating blade, as was done in the reed-type harmoniums a quarter of a century ago (Fig. 4-6).

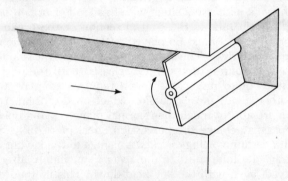

Fig. 4-6. Mechanical vibrato.

Another way of getting vibrato in some of the more expensive organs is purely mechanical—either the speaker or some kind of baffle associated with it is rotated (Fig. 4-7). The main problem is making the mechanism silent enough that it doesn't interfere with the music.

The Wurlitzer "Spectra-Tone" uses a speaker that rotates in a somewhat different mode (Fig. 4-8). This is smaller than the Leslie assembly, but achieves about the same degree of movement. This amount of movement becomes virtually meaningless as a modulator of the lower frequencies, so a different method is needed.

At low frequencies, the difference between tremolo and vibrato is difficult to discern because of the large standing waves these frequencies build up in any listening room. So a practical way to extend the effect is to apply tremolo that is electrically synchronized with the vibrato produced mechanically by the rotating speaker.

This is achieved by using a lamp, cam and a photosensitive resistor. The cam is mounted on the rotating speaker assembly, and the lamp and photosensitive resistor are fixed. With the re-

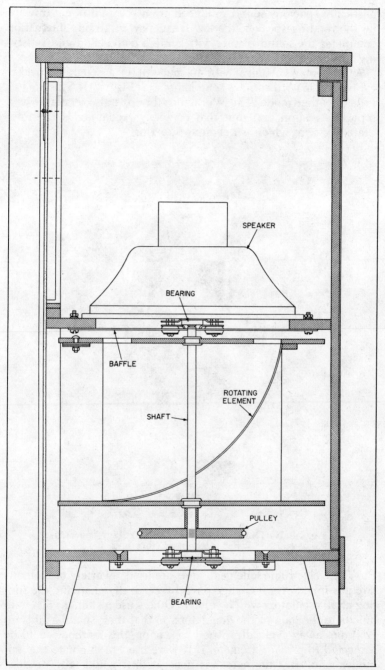

Fig. 4-7. The Baldwin-Leslie rotating mechanical-vibrato system.

alistically spacious sound produced from the mid-range upward by the rotating speaker, the low frequency amplitude fluctuation completes the sound picture with quite a convincing and satisfying illusion.

A form of mechanical vibrato, put out in a separate speaker cabinet, is made by the Allen Company (Fig. 4-9). This rotates in yet another mode. The Wurlitzer vibrato is also available as a separate, add-on unit, but that company recommends the integrated system, which is definitely superior.

Fig. 4-8. Rotating assembly of the Wurlitzer "Spectra-Tone" mechanical vibrato.

Where electronic tone generators are used, a variety of methods are possible. Several change pitch by cyclically changing the tuning of all oscillators with a voltage. Others use a similar voltage to fluctuate the gain of the generators, so that their sound builds up and dies away cyclically. Strictly speaking, this method would be expected to provide tremolo. If it were used to fluctuate the amplifier gain after the note was generated, it could only produce tremolo. But when it works on the generator itself, both pitch (or frequency) and intensity (or volume) change, giving a combination effect that is not at all unrealistic.

Where the pitch of the generator is warbled electronically, it is possible to use part of the same circuit to produce the glissando effect mentioned earlier. Some instruments incorporate this feature. To be effective, the section of the organ providing it (usually the solo or swell manual) must use separate generators for the "accompaniment."

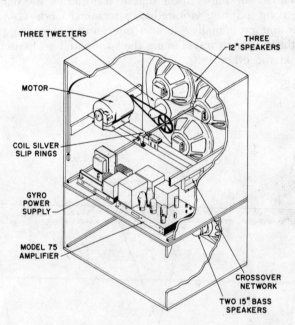

THREE TWEETERS

THREE 12" SPEAKERS

MOTOR

COIL SILVER SLIP RINGS

GYRO POWER SUPPLY

MODEL 75 AMPLIFIER

CROSSOVER NETWORK

TWO 15" BASS SPEAKERS

Fig. 4-9. Cutaway view of an Allen "Gyrophonic" external cabinet.

Earlier, the development of electronic instruments was discussed, based on a piano mechanism for the tone generation. Not to be confused with this instrument are the Story and Clark piano organs, which are really a combination of piano and organ, using the same keyboard. The piano works normally, while contacts actuated by the keys operate the electronic-organ section.

Some unique effects can be achieved with this combination. There is one drawback, however. Most of the time, the piano keys must be struck—rather than being played smoothly as is most often done with an organ. They may be held or released, depending on the music being played. On the other hand, an organ requires a steady pressure. Getting the right kind of sound from one instrument limits the range of "touch" effect possible from the other.

Reverberation

While it usually may be hidden inside a mechanical detail, many modern organs have the addition of a reverberation unit. Two principal kinds are used: mechanical transmission of vibrations corresponding to the music and tape record with playback. The mechanical part serves a different function in each.

In the mechanical transmission of vibrations, it is something equivalent to the music itself that is transmitted mechanically, usually along a spring vibrated in a torsional mode (twisting). A drive unit rotationally vibrates one end of the spring (Fig. 4-10); the vibrations travel along the spring and are sensed by a pickup at the other end.

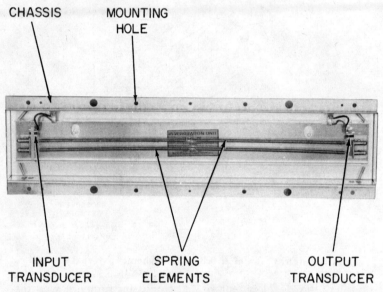

CHASSIS   MOUNTING HOLE

INPUT TRANSDUCER   SPRING ELEMENTS   OUTPUT TRANSDUCER

Fig. 4-10. A mechanical-type reverberation unit.

This kind of reverberation unit needs careful insulation from mechanical vibrations and sound waves to prevent its producing spurious effects. If it is operated without such insulation, it will produce sound like an old-fashioned bed spring, which is what it resembles, in miniature. By suitable mounting and packaging, it can be made to give quite acceptable reverberating effects.

The main advantage of the mechanical unit just described is its low cost. You might think cost would be of little importance in an electronic system that already costs probably over a thousand dollars, but cost is a very real problem in electronic organs. The cost is high, not because organ makers are greedy for profit, but because an enormous amount of electronic material of the best precision possible has to go into making an organ. So, such "trimmings" as reverberation need to be added at minimum cost to make the price reasonable.

On the other hand, the argument, "Why spoil the ship for a half-pennyworth of tar?" has some merit. For not too much more money you can get a much better form of reverberation, using a small repetitious playback tape recorder (Fig. 4-11). This has

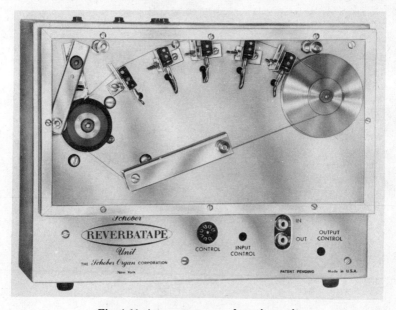

Fig. 4-11. A tape-type reverberation unit.

the advantage that individual sound reflections, simulated by the various playbacks, can be adjusted to suit the organ and its individual environment (listening room).

The unit shown (Fig. 4-11) is built by a kit manufacturer, but can be added without much difficulty to any existing organ. It comes complete with instructions for setting it up to get acceptable results, and when completed, it is quite free from the microphony that can be characteristic of the mechanical type reverberation unit.

CHAPTER 5

ORGAN ELECTRONICS

Most of the things which we have discussed are the more easily understood mechanical aspects of an organ's function. In this chapter, to complete the picture, more is presented about the remaining parts of the essential electronics that make the instrument an electronic organ.

TONE GENERATORS

The simplest electronic tone generator is the solo oscillator, which can play any note as a solo tone. This is done very simply—a relaxation or sawtooth oscillator is used wherein changing the value of one resistor changes the frequency of the sawtooth quite reliably.

Frequency is usually changed by adjusting a resistor rather than a capacitor or inductor, because it is much easier for adjustable resistors to provide the range of values needed. Figs. 5-1 and 5-2 show typical circuits for tube and transistor oscillators of this type, and Fig. 5-3 shows one that uses a neon-tube oscillator.

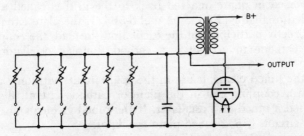

Fig. 5-1. Keying a vacuum-tube blocking oscillator.

Oscillators of this type should have a voltage-regulated power supply if the exact pitch of the notes is important—for example, where the instrument must stay in tune with other instruments, or the solo section in tune with the chord section. A change in the supply voltage will shift the whole group of tones while maintaining the correct frequency *interval* between them.

Another type of solo tone generator is shown in Fig. 5-4. It is not restricted to a sawtooth waveform, and tuning is done by adjusting the magnetic core of the inductor. The correct relationship between inductance values for the different notes is maintained by tapping the coil.

For the chord section, or harmony manual, the simplest method of tone generation uses 12 master oscillators for the top octave. Fortunately, the simpler oscillator circuits not only cost less, but are better for organs on two counts: (1) their frequency can be adjusted quite easily, usually by setting only one resistor value; and (2) by making them oscillate hard, they can be made rich in harmonics.

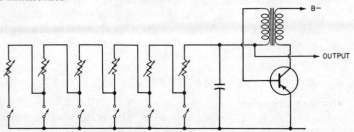

Fig. 5-2. Keying a transistorized blocking oscillator.

By using proper feedback coupling, any of the L-C oscillator circuits can be made to produce a sawtooth or relaxation type of oscillation. There are two ways of designating the type of circuit—by the way the energy is fed back, and by the arrangement of the tuned circuit.

An oscillator in which voltage from the plate circuit of a tube is reversed in phase and fed back to the grid is called a plate-coupled oscillator (Figs. 5-5A and 5-5B). If the plate circuit does not directly participate in the oscillation—instead, the coupling is from cathode to grid—it is a cathode-coupled oscillator (Fig. 5-5C).

If the tuned elements are in the grid circuit, with only a reactance or coupling coil in the plate or cathode circuit, the stage is called a tuned-grid oscillator. If the tuned elements are in the plate circuit, it is a tuned-plate oscillator.

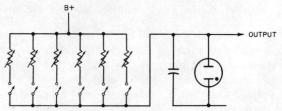

Fig. 5-3. Keying a neon-tube oscillator.

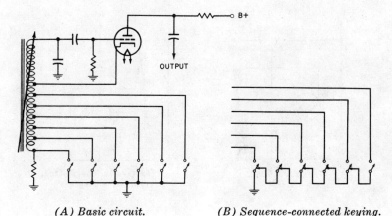

(A) Basic circuit.   (B) Sequence-connected keying.

Fig. 5-4. Keying a solo oscillator with preset taps on an inductor.

Some tuned circuits divide between the two coupled elements of the tube. In the Hartley circuit, the inductance is tapped and the capacitor in effect is across the whole inductor, from plate to grid (Fig. 5-5D) or from grid to ground (Fig. 5-5E). In the

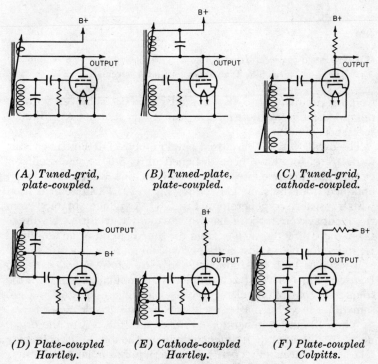

(A) Tuned-grid,
plate-coupled.

(B) Tuned-plate,
plate-coupled.

(C) Tuned-grid,
cathode-coupled.

(D) Plate-coupled
Hartley.

(E) Cathode-coupled
Hartley.

(F) Plate-coupled
Colpitts.

Fig. 5-5. Tube oscillator circuits for organ use.

71

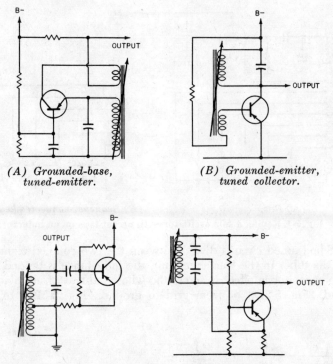

(A) Grounded-base,
tuned-emitter.

(B) Grounded-emitter,
tuned collector.

(C) Grounded-collector Hartley.

(D) Grounded-base Colpitts.

Fig. 5-6. Transistor oscillator circuits.

Colpitts circuit (Fig. 5-5F), a similar effect is achieved with an untapped inductor by using two capacitors that act as a similar reactance divider.

The oscillators just discussed employ tubes, but similar circuits using transistors have been designed (Fig. 5-6). Some oscillator circuits are arranged so that more than one waveform can be obtained from the same generator (Fig. 5-7). This circuit is used with transistorized generators (Fig. 5-8). A voltage obtained from the feedback circuit will have a sawtooth waveform. A voltage taken more directly, such as from the tuned circuit or an amplified reproduction of it, most certainly will be more nearly sinusoidal.

Resistance with the inductance of a transformer coil can also be used (Fig. 5-9), just as a simple R-L combination can form the frequency-controlling element of a blocking oscillator—a form sometimes used for master oscillators as well as solo types.

When 12 master generators are used and the rest of the organ notes are obtained by frequency dividers, the divider circuits may take several forms (Fig. 5-10). Some are quite similar to a master-oscillator circuit, using the master frequency to trigger the divider oscillator every second cycle; successive dividers use the output from the preceding divider for the same purpose. The sync signal may be coupled into the divider by a variety of methods.

When oscillator and dividers are similar, magnetically coupled coils can provide synchronization. Often, divider circuits are different from oscillator circuits. For example, neon-tube dividers are simple and will trigger reliably (Fig. 5-11).

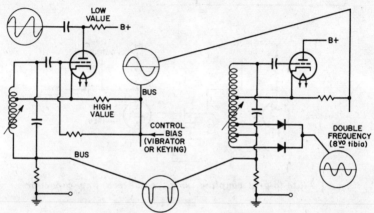

Fig. 5-7. Tube circuits with more than one output from a tone generator.

But with solid-state organs (using transistors) the bistable multivibrator has achieved considerable acceptance (Fig. 5-13). The method of coupling may vary a little, but the circuit is essentially similar to the ones shown here.

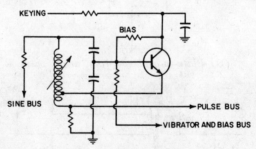

Fig. 5-8. Transistor oscillator circuit with more than one output from a tone generator.

The capacitors in these bistable units are not part of the frequency selective action, as they are with many types of dividers. Their function is to accelerate switching time in the square-wave output frequency and make locking more definite. This yields a waveform useful for later formant work.

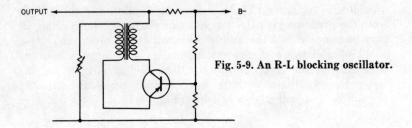

Fig. 5-9. An R-L blocking oscillator.

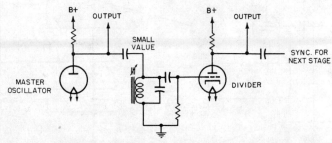

(A) Plate-to-grid coupling, small value coupling capacitor.

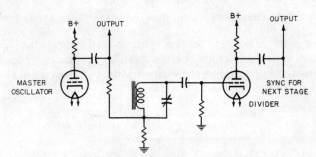

(B) Plate-to-grid coupling, small value R.

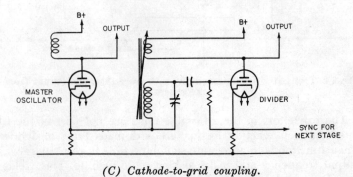

(C) Cathode-to-grid coupling.
Fig. 5-10. Methods of synchronizing divider oscillators.

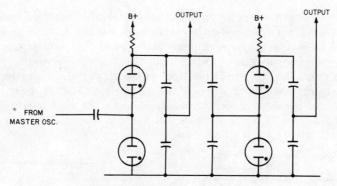

Fig. 5-11. A neon-tube divider circuit.

Without coupling from the preceding stage (the octave above), each stage would remain static, with one transistor conducting and the other one cut off, whichever way it happened to be, indefinitely. Each time a pulse is received in the triggering direction from the preceding stage (which is an octave higher than the desired output from this stage) the bistable unit flips the opposite way. So it produces a half period for each period of the previous stage.

This is an extremely reliable divider, involves no critical adjustments and is quite compact, using modern solid-state circuitry. The reason it was never used extensively with tubes is because it required a double triode for each note. Individual oscillators only required one tube (half a double triode) per oscillator. So it was more economical then, if you wanted to spend that much money, to select the individually tuned oscillators than this type of divider. This is an example of how changing technology changes design concepts as to what is the best practice.

Some organs still have separate oscillators for every note. The oscillators may be any of the types already discussed. In some instances, economy in components is affected by making one tube (or transistor) share two or more adjacent notes, on the theory that adjacent notes are seldom played together.

These sharing circuits can be any type of oscillator. Two currently in use employ additional resistors in a blocking circuit, plus tapped inductors. Fig. 5-12 shows the switching, to cover three notes with each oscillator while preventing spurious oscillations when more than one key is pressed at one time. In most organs of this type, the number of notes sharing an oscillator will vary in different parts of the keyboard.

For the pedal (bass) section, many organs use an oscillator similar to the one in the solo section, relying on only one bass note being played at a time.

In any organ where a number of notes—whether the whole solo or bass section, or a few adjacent notes in the harmony section—share an oscillator, pressing more than one of the notes in question will play only one of them, usually the highest or lowest.

So much for the purely electronic tone generator. Where tone wheels are used, 12 shafts carrying all the tone wheels must be driven at precisely stepped speeds, covering the intervals in an

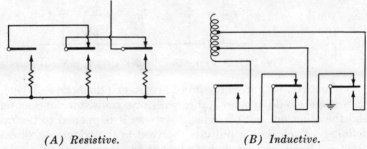

(A) Resistive.   *(B) Inductive.*

Fig. 5-12. Switching of a three-note oscillator.

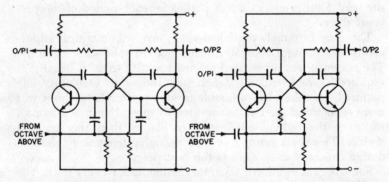

Fig. 5-13. Two variations of the bistable multivibrator frequency divider.

octave (Fig. 5-14). A belt drive gives the most uniform motion as well as conveniently providing the right steps, which would be difficult with gears.

The other main electromechanical type uses what is basically a musical tone generator such as a reed. If the vibrating part is steel or other magnetic material, the simplest conversion is magnetic, using a pickup coil and magnets. When the vibrating part is brass or other nonmagnetic material, electrostatic (capacitive) conversion, a polarizing voltage, and a coupling circuit (Fig. 5-15) will be required.

No matter whether magnetic or capacitive pickups are used, the connection to the amplifier must be properly shielded to keep

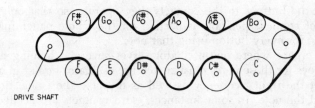

Fig. 5-14. Belt drive for mechanical generators.

out interference. In magnetic pickup circuits, use of a shielded lead and magnetic shields for the pickups is sufficient (Fig. 5-16).

For electrostatic pickups, the entire mechanism must be shielded. A convenient way to do this is to line the cabinet with a conductive coating, such as a coloidal graphite, and connect the coating to the amplifier ground (Fig. 5-17). A break due to bad contact between parts of the cabinet—e.g. where a door fits—can cause quite a bad hum in an instrument using this system.

KEYING CIRCUITS

All electronic organs use some kind of electrical contact in the keying circuits. The physical nature of these contacts may vary,

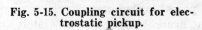

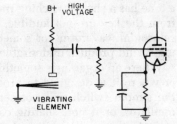

Fig. 5-15. Coupling circuit for electrostatic pickup.

but all are designed to be self-cleaning for a long, troublefree life. Some keys may use more than one contact or pair of contacts for various reasons.

In a chord organ, each note requires at least one pair of contacts. Moreover, the chord buttons must be able to play several notes simultaneously. This is often achieved by mechanically cou-

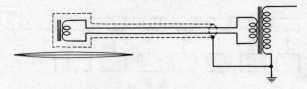

Fig. 5-16. Magnetic pickup with shielded lead.

pling the buttons to the contacts they operate, so that only one pair of contacts per note is needed for the whole panel, instead of one for every button using that note.

In organs where one oscillator serves several adjoining notes, the keys for those notes must switch the oscillator circuit in order to get the right frequency as well as to make the connection to sound the note. In some instances, extra contacts are needed for coupling.

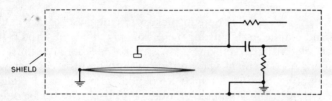

Fig. 5-17. Complete shielding for electrostatic pickups.

How does the contact attached to the key make the note sound? It varies from instrument to instrument. In the simplest organs with no provision for percussion or other effects, the keying merely closes a circuit, allowing the tone to go to the amplifier input (Fig. 5-18). For this action to be effective, the tone generators most produce a sawtooth waveform. When every cycle of a tone has a sharp switching transient, the extra sudden transients from the key are not audible; if the tone generator produced a sinusoidal waveform (or something approaching it), the switching would produce undesirable "plops" in the music.

Where an organ uses something nearer to pure-tone generators, or where it is designed to produce percussion and other effects, the simple switch will not serve. If every note has a separate oscillator, or if note-sharing oscillators are used, the switch can activate the oscillator directly.

This can be achieved in a variety of ways. The key switch can connect the B+ to the tube plate (Fig. 5-19A). If a pentode is used, the key switch may connect the B+ to the screen (Fig. 5-19B), thus making it easier to avoid any "plops." Or the key may switch out a negative bias applied to the control grid (Fig. 5-19C).

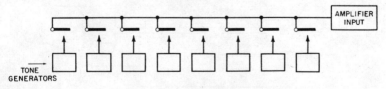

Fig. 5-18. A simple form of keying.

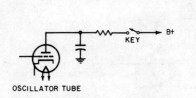

(A) In the plate circuit.

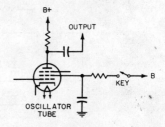

(B) In the screen circuit.

Fig. 5-19. Methods of keying a tone oscillator.

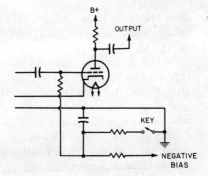

(C) In the grid circuit.

In organs that have 12 master tone generators for the whole organ or some main part of it, the tones themselves cannot be switched on and off; they must be left running continuously, because they may be needed in other octaves. In circuits of this type, the key switches control amplifier stages; these are normally biased to cutoff, allowing no tone to get through. When the key is closed, the tube is biased to amplify the tone with its normal gain, adding it to whatever other tones may be going into the main amplifier (Fig. 5-20).

Modern technology has made changes here, too. As well as tiny transistors, solid-state developments include yet smaller di-

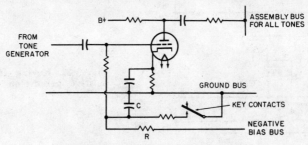

Fig. 5-20. Keying for a sustain effect.

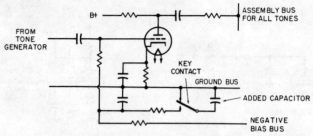

Fig. 5-21. Keying for a single percussive effect.

odes that can be packaged into gating circuits. This circuit already described (Fig. 3-12) shows how it can be used for sustain effect.

In bias keying, a "sustain" effect can be obtained by adding a capacitor in the bias circuit so that the tone dies away gradually after the switch has been opened. Values of R and C determine how long the note sustains after the key is released. A more definite percussive effect can be had by arranging the key switch so it does not provide a DC closed circuit, but discharges the bias capacitor and immediately allows it to start charging again (Fig. 5-21). Only repeated playing of the note will make the tone repeatedly "strike" at full intensity.

A further refinement provides a multivibrator output that can take the place of the steady bias voltage when the key is pressed, thus giving a rapid repeated percussion effect like that of a xylophone or marimba (Fig. 5-22) while the key is held down.

TONE FORMANTS

After the outputs from all the notes played on one manual or from the chord panel have been mixed and amplified, they are passed through one or more networks (in parallel) of formant circuits that closely simulate the frequency spectrum, or tone coloration, of various instruments. Much more complicated cir-

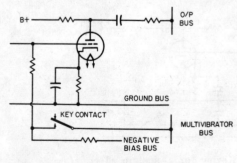

Fig. 5-22. Keying for repetitive percussion effect.

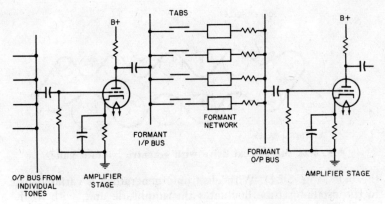

Fig. 5-23. General arrangement of formant selectors.

cuits could probably be used; but beyond a certain point, further complexity would make little noticeable difference in the sound.

Different formant circuits are usually provided for each section of the organ, but all the notes of a section are combined first and passed through one formant circuit. Output from the formant circuits is combined, so that combination tone qualities can be achieved for greater variety (Fig. 5-23).

VIBRATO AND TREMOLO

Musically, vibrato means fluctuation in pitch, and tremolo refers to fluctuation in intensity. However, few circuits do either one exclusively. Actually, though, this is not too important because the two effects sound quite similar.

A rhythmic intensity fluctuation is essentially a very low-frequency amplitude modulation; the frequency fluctuation is similarly a frequency modulation. In an electrical circuit, the main difference between amplitude and frequency modulation is the phase of the sidebands. Because music is in the form of sound waves, the phase can become almost anything, because of room reflections. What may be radiated as pure vibrato can appear as tremolo at some particular listening spot, and as vibrato elsewhere. In short, it is not too important to produce either pure tremolo or pure vibrato.

Vibrato or tremolo circuits, like other means of modulating tones, can be achieved in two ways in electronic organs—apart from the mechanical method of spinning a speaker or a baffle plate.

The most obvious method is to warble the pitch of the tone generators themselves, or to swing the amplitude of oscillation. With mechanical tone generators, this is achieved by wobbling

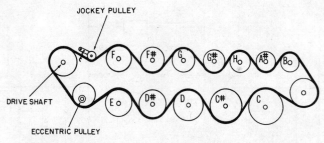

Fig. 5-24. Mechanical drive with eccentric vibrato pulley.

the belt (Fig. 5-24). With electronic generators, a variable bias to the oscillator tube fluctuates the amplitude and, with it, the pitch (Fig. 5-25). Varying the bias on a capacitor control diode, at the vibrato-rate, modulates the pitch by changing the amount of capacitance in the tuned circuit (Fig. 5-26).

Each of these methods works equally well, whether separate oscillators are used for every note, or 12 master oscillators with

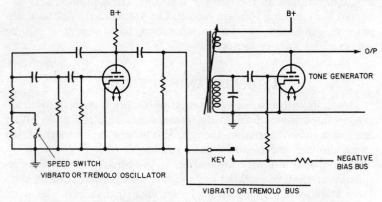

Fig. 5-25. Vibrato system using control generator.

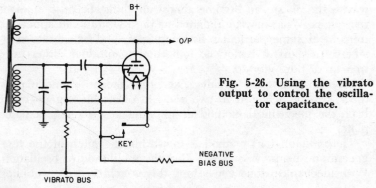

Fig. 5-26. Using the vibrato output to control the oscillator capacitance.

frequency dividers. When the frequency is divided, any swing in pitch is divided with the pitch.

In the second electronic method of adding vibrato or tremolo, the tone generators operate on a fixed frequency and amplitude, but the tone is changed in the amplifier. This has the advantage that parts of the organ can be given vibrato or tremolo from the same tone generators.

Fluctuation in amplitude is achieved in much the same way as with oscillator tubes—by varying the bias. If the keys control an amplifier stage, the tremolo can be introduced at the keys, just as percussion is. Vibrato is a little more difficult to do this way. The usual method is to introduce a variable phase-shift network,

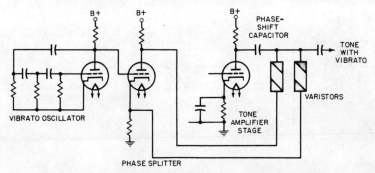

Fig. 5-27. Using a variable phase-shift network to introduce vibrato.

which can be controlled by a variable bias voltage. In this instance it is advantageous to use a push-pull vibrato mixing circuit, to keep low-frequency thumping out of the organ voice (Fig. 5-27).

EXPRESSION CONTROL

The pedal that controls the volume is usually called the "swell" on pipe organs. In electronic organs, it is usually called "expression," although some manufacturers still use the more classical term. It is nothing more than a volume control like that of a hi-fi set, only operated by a foot bar or pedal (Fig. 5-28) instead of a knob.

In most modern organs, a capacitive control is used (Fig. 5-29) because it has no movable contact. The swell pedals are played so repeatedly that a resistive control is likely to become noisy after a few years.

Where the resistive-type swell control is still employed, a limiting resistor is sometimes used with it. A swell control should not make the organ go off, but merely make it play very quietly.

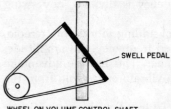

SWELL PEDAL

WHEEL ON VOLUME CONTROL SHAFT

Fig. 5-28. Simplest form of swell (expression) control.

Using a capacitor in conjunction with a limiting resistor permits loudness compensation for the bass frequencies, so that the music does not sound "thin" when played quietly (Fig. 5-30).

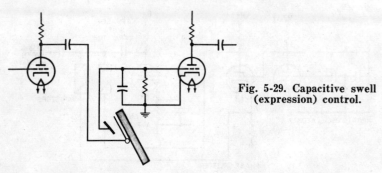

Fig. 5-29. Capacitive swell (expression) control.

Amplifiers

Amplifiers for electronic organs are much like amplifiers for high fidelity, stereo or public address work; they can be either tube or transistor. Here should be answered some common questions about which kind is the better, and how much power is needed.

As to which is the better, the consensus is for transistors. A few diehards stick by tubes, as "more reliable" (they claim). Actually it is doubtful if this reason stands. On the other side of the coin, transistors are very much more compact, enabling much "more" organ to be built within a given size; they are never micro-

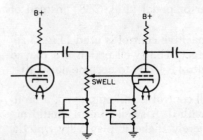

B+   B+

SWELL

Fig. 5-30. Resistive swell control.

phonic, as tubes become. Microphonic tubes cause spurious howls at the worst, and spoil the quality in any event. Everyone seems to concede that transistors sound much "cleaner," for this reason.

How much power is needed? There is no simple answer to this question. To say that the audio power should be adequate does not answer the question, but poses another: how much is adequate? There are two ways of going about providing adequate power: with one big amplifier or a number of small ones.

Some advocate one big amplifier, of say 100 watts, in preference to several smaller ones. But let's make a comparison. Suppose another make of organ has three 15-watt amplifiers. They could be 25-watt amplifiers, which would still only total 75 watts, against the 100 watts in the single big one.

In the three-amplifier organ, one plays the swell, or solo manual, one the accompaniment, or great manual, and one the bass, or pedal organ.

In practically any organ music you play, you will use all three parts of the organ at once: each will be producing its own music. So, with 15-watt amplifiers you can have 15 watts of pedal organ, 15 watts of great organ, and 15 watts of swell organ, a total of 45 watts. Or if they are 25-watt units, the total is 75 watts.

On the face of it, this will not equal the "power" of the organ with a single 100-watt amplifier. But now think what happens when you feed the same total music (rather than power) into one amplifier. To make the figuring definite and simple, suppose the speakers are 15-ohm units (one per amplifier, or arranged so the total amplifier loads have this value). Across a 15-ohm load, 15 watts produces 15 volts.

The system has to handle the combined waveform, which is in either volts or current, not watts. Adding together $15 + 15 + 15$ makes 45 volts that the combined unit has to handle, to equal the music power delivered by the individual 15-watt units all together. And 45 volts across 15 ohms(this would have to be made up with more speakers to handle the power) is not 45 watts, but 135 watts.

So the three 15-watt amplifiers, each handling their own part of the music, can put out as much as one 135 watt amplifier handling it alone. The three 25-watt amplifiers, by the same token, would put out the equivalent of a single amplifier rated, not at 75 watts, but at 225 watts. When you think of it that way, you realize that the single 100-watt amplifier, impressive as its rating may sound, may not be the best buy.

Speakers

Multiple-speaker systems are used in most organs to widen the radiation effect. A good many instruments have one or two large (12" or 15") speakers for the low frequencies, one or more medium-sized (8" or 10") speakers for the medium range, and smaller high-frequency speakers. These may be mounted within the organ, in a separate cabinet, or both. Where extra power is required, an auxiliary amplifying system is used. It may be one large enclosure with amplifier and built-in multiple-speaker system, or an elaborate arrangement of booster amplifiers and remote speakers.

Power Supplies

Earlier organs required most demanding power-supply units. More recent designs, using transistors, have simpler supplies. The better organs either use a single regulated supply for the whole organ, or have transistor regulator circuits (Fig. 5-31), usually

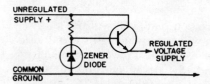

Fig. 5-31. The basic elements of a regulated voltage supply.

using a zener diode to set the voltage with an emitter follower to provide the needed current at that controlled voltage.

Such regulated voltages do not always constitute the entire supply, because of the large rating which the emitter follower would need. Instead, supplies are regulated for just those parts of a circuit for which constant or controlled voltage is necessary. A number of different stabilized and regulated voltages may be drawn from the same basic supply to serve a circuit requiring so many carefully balanced voltages.

CHAPTER 6

CHOOSING AN ORGAN

In the previous two chapters we discussed the various ways in which organs can differ. Now comes the question of choosing one for your own needs. Which organ is going to suit your individual requirements, and how much can you afford to pay for it? You may want to listen to several representative organs. This may entail visiting several dealers, to see just how much the differences

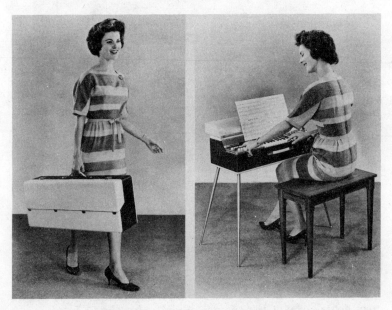

Fig. 6-1. Orcoa *Travler* portable organ.

we have discussed mean to you, and what combinations of features will suit you best—both as to cost and playing convenience. To one person, full regular organ features—two manuals and pedal bass, as well as buttons for bass and chords (Fig. 4-4)—may seem essential. To another, where the organ is to be a less serious hobby, a chord organ with the simplest playing features (Fig.

6-1), will be more important than the ability to expand his playing prowess later.

There are enough electronic organ manufacturers to make the business quite competitive. So, in answer to the "how much" question, you really get as much organ as you pay for. You should decide which of the features you desire are worth their cost. To one person, the tonal quality—the extra "body"—achieved by an organ with separate tone generators (Fig. 6-2) for every note is

Fig. 6-2. Conn organ with individual generators for each note.

virtually a must, however much more it may cost. Another person may actually favor the simpler organ with only 12 basic generators (Fig. 6-3) and frequency dividers, even if cost were not a factor. This is something you can decide only by listening.

To aid in comparison of organs, we strongly recommend you try them yourself, even though you may be unfamiliar with keyboard instruments. Don't compare just by having the salesmen demonstrate to you. You are more likely to judge by their relative playing skills than by the comparative qualities of the organs themselves. Even if you feel you "can't play a note," have a try. Press some of the keys and flip the tabs, to see what changes of tonal quality you get. Check the features discussed in the previous two chapters. This will give you the "feel" of the organ. By trying several organs in this way, you will get a better idea of which one will suit you best.

Fig. 6-3. Orcoa *Concert* chord organ with 12 master generators.

The simplest organs will probably give most people the most fun for their money. Features that add $100 or more to an organ may not seem worth that much extra to you. If so, then buy a simple, inexpensive organ. The difference between organs from a reputable manufacturer (Figs. 6-4, 6-5) is not one of quality, but of quantity. The least expensive organ is as good and reliable as the best model in the same line—it merely has fewer features. If those extra features seem to be "gilt on the gingerbread," you don't need them.

Suppose, however, that you want something a little better than the most inexpensive. You compare models, and note that the expensive organs are much more versatile. You don't want to pay the highest price, but you'd like the best you can afford.

You have a choice, starting with any one of a number of really low-cost organs that have minimum facilities but are capable of producing quite pleasing music, and progressing (with various additions and in various combinations) up to ambitious organs costing between $1,000 and $2,000 (Fig. 6-6). Nor do you have to stop there, of course, if you have the money to spend and a

Fig. 6-4. Estey organ with rotary-switch voice stops.

place to put one of the big professional organs. Some important features such as formant circuits provide quite a range of tone-color variation—at least enough so that you hear the difference when you flip the tabs—yet do not cost very much, and all except perhaps a few of the least expensive organs will have six or more voices of this type. But some of the more definite tone-character features, such as the addition of sustain and/or percussion effects, are more expensive to incorporate.

Percussion has a great attraction for most people. But beware of accepting an organ that merely claims to include this feature.

Until recently, percussion has never been achieved electronically. Recent developments have produced some quite convincing imitations. Organs that merely have a sustain feature sometimes call that percussion, when in reality it has no truly percussive effect whatever. A true percussive effect requires something more than sustain, and organs that include such a feature have different names for this extra quality.

Vibrato is incorporated on more organs than some other tonal-quality features, because its effect is much more noticeable. The

Fig. 6-5. Estey organ with tab switches.

important things to look for in vibrato are smoothness and uniformity. Some vibratos are jerky—the pitch does not waver up and down smoothly. Others work more effectively on the lower than on the higher notes, or vice versa—or maybe with an erratic effect not directly related to the pitch of the notes.

These distinctions can easily be overlooked at first, unless you listen quite carefully. You may be listening for many things. So you flip the Vibrato tab and find that the vibrato is there in one position, but not in the other—without paying too much attention to quality. In other words, to get your money's worth in buying an organ, you need to listen critically. Otherwise, something you didn't notice at first may ultimately give you dissatisfaction.

The Heath Company now issues kits which enable the purchaser to build one of the organs designed by the Thomas Company. At the other end of the range, if you want to build something far more ambitious than you can afford "ready-made", or build one with features of your own choosing, the Artisan Company has a complete range of parts so that you can design, as well as build, your own organ. Their "Organ Builder's Manual" explains what you can do and how to do it.

Even though there is plenty of choice in ready-made organs, there is another possibility—build your own! At one time, that would have been a project to be undertaken only by an electronic engineer. But the advent of organ kits, such as those offered by the Schober Organ Company, has made the task much easier. It's an excellent proposition—if you have more spare time than spare

Fig. 6-6. Magnavox electronic organ.

money, and if you enjoy projects of this nature. There's a lot of work in building one of these organs, but they're relatively simple if taken a little at a time and if the directions are followed. The kits can be bought complete (which cuts down the shipping cost) or a piece at a time (which enables the cost to be spread out).

From two basic models, additional features can be added so that a choice almost comparable to that of most ready-made lines is available. When you build your own, you also have to tune it. However, the manufacturer makes this relatively easy by providing you with a tuning kit.

Fig. 6-7. Thomas *Serenade.*

Some decisions will be based on your own personality. The simpler organs are easier to play for those with little or no experience. If you haven't the patience to gain experience, one of the simpler organs may be a better choice. It certainly would be impractical to buy an organ with a full pedal section, yet never have the patience to learn to play it! Bass from buttons, along with the chord-button panel, would be easier for you. With a

Schober Recital Organ. A custom organ for the kitbuilder using master oscillator design.

Conn Minuet, Model 542. A popular home model using independent tone generators.

A transistorized Artisan Theater organ using individual tone generators.

Gulbranson Model 5. Completely transistorized with individual tone generators.

Lowrey Starlet deluxe.

Thomas Fiesta, Model AR-2.
The all-transistorized budget
model of the Thomas line.

Allen Sheraton 15. One of the
Allen line of transistor organs.

Model GD-983 produced by Heathkit to designs by Thomas for home organ builders.

Wurlitzer Model 4017. A simpler model for the budget customer.

Hammond L-133 organ using the drawbar tone synthesis.

minimum of effort, you'll be able to make quite pleasant sounding music from such an organ.

On the other hand, if you are somewhat of a perfectionist, you'll definitely want an organ with more features. Sooner or later, the simpler organ will restrict your ambitions, whereas the one providing greater flexibility offers you more of a challenge.

An organ with a wide range of voices, percussion effects (Fig. 6-7), etc., needs a somewhat more ambitious player to get the best from it. If you merely want to be able to "play a tune," these varied effects will be unnecessary. But if you want to play music with all its variations, the different voices and other features will be essential. Organs using reed tone generators have the advantage of giving a full-bodied sound because of their large number of generators. Because of the differences in the waveform and in the voicing circuits, the range of tone colors will differ from those produced by electronic oscillators. Your organist friends may find the reed sound distasteful, although your ears have become accustomed to it.

If you want an organ that is easy to play, one of the chord organs should be your choice. You may prefer the straight-forward button panel, the button panel with rhythm bar and two bass pedals, or the simple keyboard with chord-playing features.

If you want to start fairly easily but not be limited to the effects a chord organ can create, then you need a combination instrument that provides the chord-organ feature plus full keyboard and pedal facilities.

CHAPTER 7

TUNING THE ORGAN

Until recently, tuning any musical instrument was regarded as professional work, requiring a very sensitive ear to correctly adjust the instrument to the proper pitch on every note. Now the sheer number of instruments has made it necessary for others to "get into the act." Technicians, as well as professional tuners, must know something about tuning.

We will not suggest that you try to rely on your ear, as a professional tuner does. This requires years of training and practice. But there are instrumental methods that can help in various ways. In magazines, describing the different methods, claims have been made for the relative accuracy of different methods; these need evaluating. Before describing any of them, however, we should emphasize that the most precise method can only be as accurate as the degree to which care is taken in applying it.

The first instrumental aid to tuning has been available for some years, it is called the *Stroboconn*, made by Conn (Fig. 7-1). This uses stroboscopic discs, similar to the ones used to set your phonograph turntable speed with a 60-cycle light set to the correct speed, but driven from a motor supplied by an amplifier whose output frequency is derived from a tuning fork.

A microphone (or for electronic organ work, direct connection is possible) with another amplifier makes neon lamps, illuminating the discs, flicker at the frequency of the note played. When the two frequencies agree, because the note is in tune, the appropriate pattern appears to stand still. If it appears to drift one way or the other, the note is sharp or flat, and an adjustment to make the pattern stand still tells just how much it is sharp or flat.

A less expensive version of the *Stroboconn* is the *Strobotuner* (Fig. 7-2), which has only one tuning window instead of twelve and which does not include a tuning fork drive. However, its accuracy is within 5 percent or 1/20th of a semitone (the interval between adjacent notes). Otherwise the method is quite similar to that used with the *Stroboconn*.

Fig. 7-1. The *Stroboconn* tuning aid by Conn Organ Co.

Various other methods have been suggested that depend on counting beats between different notes in various ways; and this undoubtedly can give correct tuning when carefully applied.

However, Richard Dorf, designer of the Schober line of organs for kit builders, has designed a strobe tuner called the *Autotuner* (Fig. 7-3) that is particularly well adapted for the master oscillator type of organ which constitutes a large proportion today. With not too much difficulty it can be used for those with individually tuned notes throughout the scale.

Rather than using separate discs for each note or varying the speed of the same disc for different notes, this instrument uses a

Fig. 7-2. The *Strobotuner* by Conn Organ Co.

Fig. 7-3. The *Autotuner* a product of Schober Organ Co.

single disc with 12 bands on it. The synchronous motor drives the whole disc at precisely 60 rpm—1 revolution every second. This is not quite as fast as the old 78 rpm phonograph records used

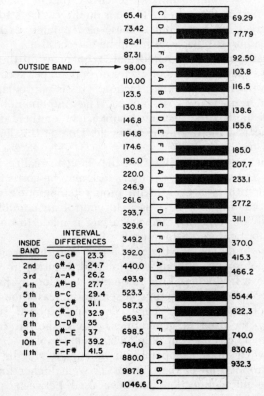

OUTSIDE BAND		
65.41	C	69.29
73.42	D	77.79
82.41	E	
87.31	F	92.50
98.00	G	103.8
110.00	A	116.5
123.5	B	
130.8	C	138.6
146.8	D	155.6
164.8	E	
174.6	F	185.0
196.0	G	207.7
220.0	A	233.1
246.9	B	
261.6	C	277.2
293.7	D	311.1
329.6	E	
349.2	F	370.0
392.0	G	415.3
440.0	A	466.2
493.9	B	
523.3	C	554.4
587.3	D	622.3
659.3	E	
698.5	F	740.0
784.0	G	830.6
880.0	A	932.3
987.8	B	
1046.6	C	

INSIDE BAND	INTERVAL DIFFERENCES	
	G–G#	23.3
2nd	G#–A	24.7
3rd	A–A#	26.2
4th	A#–B	27.7
5th	B–C	29.4
6th	C–C#	31.1
7th	C#–D	32.9
8th	D–D#	35
9th	D#–E	37
10th	E–F	39.2
11th	F–F#	41.5

Fig. 7-4. The frequencies and notes used with the *Autotuner.*

to spin. This disc is illuminated by a neon tube, lit by a special saturated amplifier contained in the instrument. The notes, with their frequencies used for tuning are shown (Fig. 7-4).

The outermost disc carries a pattern that stands still when the bass note G is played (98 periods per second). This will tune all the G's in the scale, automatically if the organ uses master oscillators, or by octave zero-beating, if it has individual oscillators.

Now we proceed from a G note two octaves higher, by playing adjacent notes, producing beats. These are not the kind of beats used for aural tuning, being much too fast to hear, but beats that the saturated amplifier in the instrument will detect and feed to the neon light for the strobe to indicate.

First, we play G and G♯ together, and adjust the pitch of the G♯ oscillator for the inside pattern on the strobe disc to stand still. Next, we play G♯ and A together, and adjust the pitch of the A♯ oscillator for the pattern next to the inside on the strobe disc to stand still. In this way, adjoining pairs of notes are played, using successive bands until we reach F♯, tuning it against F on the band next to the outside. There is no direct check for the final scale interval, F♯ to G, but if these eleven intervals have been correctly adjusted, the twelfth will be correct also.

The reader may have noted that frequencies on the scale are not always exact numbers of cycles or periods per second—sometimes they include a decimal fraction. This is particularly true at the lower frequencies (bass notes). The *Autotuner*, by its very design, is limited to checking frequencies (or their differences, to be exact) to the nearest exact cycle. Doesn't this limit the accuracy of the instrument?

In evaluating a thing like this, the thing to realize is that accuracy is always relative. A tuning fork may be correct to within one hundredth of a cycle, with proper temperature compensation and control. But it is used to control an amplifier, which may "pull" the fork's frequency—in fact is made to do so—when detuned to measure off-tune error.

Similarly a device like the *Strobotuner* can run at only limited accuracy of speed, although its internal accuracy is within 0.5 percent of a frequency. Line frequency occasionally jumps a little, but even with these jumps, it seldom increases more than 0.1 percent of its rated frequency. The old-fashioned supply frequency meter used in generating stations, showed frequencies from 55 to 65 cps for controlling a 60-cycle supply.

Even when supply companies ran independently, the frequency seldom dropped lower than 59 cps, or went higher than 61 cps. But since interconnection has been used between quite large systems, much closer frequency control became necessary to stabilize the system. Nowadays the frequency seldom deviates by more than 0.1 percent, or 0.06 cycle, from 59.94 cycles to 60.04 cycles.

So a synchronously driven disc will hold everything within this absolute, or reference accuracy, which is closer than either the *Stroboconn* or *Strobotuner* can guarantee. The fact that there are fractions of a cycle on frequencies in the 400-cycle region means that the *Autotuner* must tune to the nearest cycle, assuming everything else is absolutely "on". This is always less than half a cycle, because we take it to the nearest cycle on difference frequency. So the error is always less than 0.5 cycle in 400 cycles on any one tuning; this is close to 0.1 percent.

The choice seems reminiscent of the precision engineer, who machined a metal part to within a millionth of an inch of correct dimension, but then discovered his dimension was one whole inch "off!" Maybe the man who was satisfied with being correct to only one ten-thousandth of an inch was a little nearer the correct dimension.

There are protagonists for both ways of doing the job. As we said at the outset, each can only be as good as the way it is done. With an appropriate degree of skill, both methods of tuning can be quite precise enough.

For those who want to try the aural-beat method, we will give a couple of tabulations prepared by those who have used them, which really are variations of the same basic method. This approach always uses the musical "fifth" interval, which typically is that between the notes C and G, and closely approximates a frequency ratio of 2:3. The departure from an exact 2:3 ratio produces a beat, between the third harmonic of the lower frequency and the second harmonic of the upper one.

The academic fifth is a ratio of 2:3 or 1:1.5 (for simplicity in writing, we'll just call it 1.5), while the tempered fifth, on which the modern musical scale is based, is actually 1.4983. . . . If the actual frequencies were 1000 and 1498.3 (which are not notes actually used, but are convenient for illustration), there would be 3000 cycles of the third harmonic of the lower frequency and 2996.6 cycles of the second harmonic of the higher frequency. This will produce a beat of 3.4 warbles per second.

It is difficult to count the warbling beats per second with any accuracy, so the usual method is to count for a longer period. There are two ways: one is to count the beats in five or ten seconds. For a rate of 3.4 beats per second there would be 17 beats in 5 seconds, or 34 beats in 10 seconds. The other way counts, say, ten beats, checking the time in seconds.

Counting the beats in a number of seconds works better for high frequencies, yielding a larger number of beats, while counting the seconds for a given number of beats gives greater accu-

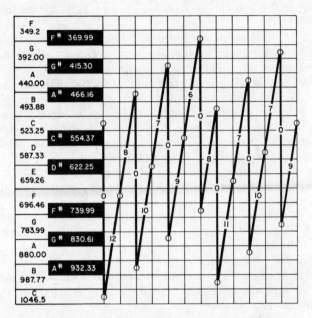

Fig. 7-5. A chart for tuning by counting beats for 5 seconds.

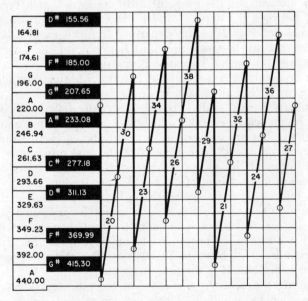

Fig. 7-6. A chart for counting time (in seconds) for 10 beats.

racy with lower frequencies, to give a longer time with greater precision. Charts for the two counting methods (Figs. 7-5 and 7-6) are shown.

When using either beat-counting method, be sure the beat you count is on the right side of zero. The notes should be closer together than zero beat, by the number specified. This means the upper note should be low (flat) or the lower note high (sharp) by this many beats.

To be sure of this you need to know which way the tuning control works. Usually turning the tuning control clockwise raises the frequency, counterclockwise lowers it, but you should be sure. Play the note you are about to tune (not the one already tuned) by itself and turn the tuning control. You will soon find which way to turn it to raise or lower the pitch.

Having ascertained this, tune the note through zero beat with the one against which you are checking, and then detune it on the near side (which is low if you are tuning the upper note of a pair, according to the methods described here) until you get the correct beat rate.

Each of these methods—the *Autotuner* and the beat-counting methods—works well with master-oscillator–type organs, where all the notes of a given name are tuned at once because they are tied together in precise 2:1 (octave) ratio by frequency dividers. With organs using individual oscillators for every note there is more work—as there is regardless of the system of tuning used.

Having tuned an octave, or an octave and a half, as the case may be, by the beat-counting process, octaves on either side, above and below the section initially tuned, are found by zero beating. This is even more difficult, in some respects, but is more reliable than any other way.

When notes an octave apart are played together, a zero beat should result—both notes sound in complete unison, without any beat at all. In practice, one tunes the note to be tuned past the half or double frequency of the one already tuned, and endeavors to find zero beat as the note goes through it.

As you tune, the beat will get slower and slower and slower, until it stops, or appears to. Then, as you tune further, it will start again, and increase its speed. The problem is that precise zero is difficult to identify, especially since there sometimes may be a tendency to "lock" when the two are played together and the beat is slow or close.

When this happens note carefully at what point in the rotation of the tuning adjustment frequency that locking occurs, as you approach it from each direction. The correct tuning will usually be a position located centrally between these two settings.

CHAPTER 8

PLAYING THE ORGAN

For all the popularity of electronic organs, a considerable proportion of them end up as status symbols—and rather expensive ones at that. The purchaser undoubtedly visualized being able to play the organ. And the salesman on the showroom floor undoubtedly encouraged that ambition, at least to the point of sale. But then came the moment of truth, when the prospective buyer would like to hear himself "try it out." Then he may have realized that it's not as easy as it looks.

LEARNING TO PLAY

To overcome this sales resistance, the organ companies included lesson courses with the sale, either at a nominal extra, or "free," included in the price of the organ. With a little assurance that the purchaser could play "this well" after six (or however many) "easy lessons," the sale was made.

How "Easy" Are the Easy Lessons?

The truth is, learning is not difficult. There are many things all of us have learned to do that are more difficult than playing an electronic organ, So the salesman was not actually misleading in his claims. However, the approach adopted in presenting the lessons may be a little misleading.

These days the demand is for "instant" everything, from coffee to TV dinners to education (which we'd like to have). So the courses have been aimed to present a way of "instant playing." As far as they go, this may work. But to become as proficient as almost anyone soon wants to become, requires more work than some promises imply is necessary—and a lot of practice.

The easy part comes quickly: you can play a few popular melodies, such as "I Left My Heart in San Francisco", using specially written music to make it easy, with a degree of seeming proficiency, in no time flat; but then you want to become more proficient. The easy effects, given in the early lessons, don't seem as spectacular as you first thought they did and you'd like to do some other wonderful things you know the instrument can do.

The "easy lessons" should be regarded as stepping stones to the more difficult things. The *Pointer* system, much of which concentrates on helping you to play chords correctly and easily, should not be treated as an end in itself. If you do this, you will learn to play only simple things set to music arranged according to the system. Other music will be outside your sphere of ability, however simple it may really be in itself.

Rather, you should regard the *Pointer* system, or any other system of learning to play, as a way of learning to visualize what music really is. By this means you will learn to recognize chords any way they happen to be written, and, likewise, to play them in their various forms.

Practice in Private

One of the problems about learning to play is the same one prospective violinists have: they can't be proficient all at once and, until they are, they can be a "pain!" With the violin this is inevitable, we suppose. But with the electronic organ it isn't.

You may be self-conscious about practising with others listening. And if you are not, others may find it trying, unless you are much quicker than most of us at mastering the difficult spots! With electronic organs, there is a way around this problem whereby you can practice privately, in silence, even in a roomful of people!

To do this requires a pair of headphones and some resistors. If you are a nontechnical reader, get a technician to set this up for you. If you are a technician, you can set it up for your organ owning customers.

In its simplest form, you disconnect the speakers and connect dummy load resistors of values equal to the nominal impedance of the speakers and of adequate wattage rating to handle the power for which the amplifiers are rated. Then you bridge the various outputs with limiting resistors, so the headphones get a balanced mixture of the organ's total output (Fig. 8-1). These resistors should be installed in pairs of equal value, chosen so that the headphones output level from each section of the organ sounds about the same loudness as the speakers do when connected. The best way to install such an arrangement is to include switching, so the whole thing can be changed over any time, according to whether you want to practice or play "out loud" (Fig. 8-2).

An Inexpensive Electronic "Teacher"

The learner is now able to practice silently, in private, even when other people are around. But there is one more thing the electronic technician can do if there is a tape recorder around.

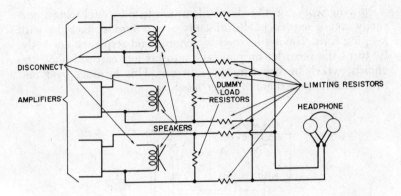

Fig. 8-1. Basic method for connecting headphones in place of speakers.

Another problem the learner has is with coordination—getting all the parts to work together: right hand on the swell or solo manual, left hand on the accompaniment or great manual, and feet on the pedals, left for the bass and right for the swell or volume.

The recorder can help by "remembering" some of the parts while the learner works on others. Wire it so the organ can be recorded silently, as well as being listened to. Also wire it so that it can be played back silently (which most recorders can, just by plugging in headphones, which disconnects the internal speakers). Include an arrangement so that the left ear hears the recorder while the right ear hears the organ (Fig. 8-3).

Now the learner can work like this: first be learns to play the melody of a piece with his right hand on the swell manual. When he has this nicely learned so he can repeat it correctly without difficulty, he turns on the recorder and records this part.

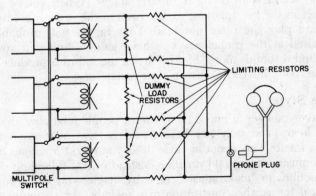

Fig. 8-2. A permanent "learning" installation with switch and socket for headphones.

Now he works on the chords, learning to play each chord correctly and in sequence. His difficulty now will most likely be with keeping time. Having learned the chords and sequence correctly, he turns the recorder on playback into his left ear and plays the chords, which he hears in his right ear. This he does over and over until he gets them together nicely.

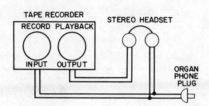

Fig. 8-3. "Learning" aid with recorder and stereo headphones added.

Now it is fairly easy to put the two hands together: each part has been learned separately and both hands "know what they have to do." Practice this a few times and then record it. If you want, you may be able to put some expression in with the right foot on the swell pedal. But it is still difficult to fit in the bass while doing all those other things. So record all you have done so far.

Now you can play back everything except the bass, concentrating on getting the bass correct with your left foot. That is relatively easy. After a little practice you will be able to complete the piece with everything but bass prerecorded, while you play the bass with it. Now put the whole thing together "live." In much less time than you think, you will be playing the whole thing, quite proficiently.

The secret is in doing it in easy stages. When you've got it perfect in the headphones, switch back to the organ's loudspeakers and play the piece out loud. Your family will probably be surprised at the proficiency you have gained, and you yourself will find it sounds more "lifelike" when the sound is produced out in the room, instead of just in your headphones.

Free Style

Have you ever admired the talent of people who play anything they hear (and may not have heard before) without needing music for it? This is not as difficult as you might imagine. If you learn music, theory and practice, instead of just following simple instructions to "make music," as if by magic, you will recognize musical forms, the constitution of a melody, the structure of its supporting chords, or harmony, any time you hear a piece,

110

whether it is familiar to you or something new. This will enable you to go home and play the same piece on your own organ, with little practice, once you have become proficient at playing by music.

CHAPTER 9

GENERAL MAINTENANCE AND TROUBLESHOOTING

Although electronic organs contain many parts, they are not as complicated as they look at first glance. For one thing, many of the circuits are duplicated several times. For example, all the tone circuits are very similar electrically. Yet, by tuning each one to a different note, they can be made to produce the whole set of tones; it isn't necessary to use a different type of tone circuit for each note.

Tuning is about the only routine maintenance an organ is likely to need. But there may be quite extensive possibilities for troubleshooting. Generally speaking, electronic organs give little trouble. But when they do, there are so many places where the trouble could be that troubleshooting (see Chapter 7) may be quite an operation.

Once you understand the basic connection used in the instrument, troubleshooting will usually prove to be 90 percent circuit tracing, to see where signals "disappear." If you have a schematic —or set of schematics, as is usually the case—such tracing will be easier. Most organ makers supply schematics only to accredited service agents, and the service manual gives most of the hints you need to trace the more common faults.

In such manuals, the service instructions often are limited to trying new tubes in defective oscillators or other sections. In solid state circuits, the schematic usually carries voltage check details which help in troubleshooting. If this fails to correct the condition, the manual instructs the service technician to install a new unit in that section. It is best to follow this advice, especially where printed circuitry is used, because the warranty often states that the printed circuit is guaranteed for a certain length of time—in some cases five years—and this guarantee becomes void if the printed board has been tampered with.

Apart from this, the factory has the specialized test equipment to ensure that each part matches the operation of the other circuits in the organ. However, the foregoing checking procedure will prove helpful in pinpointing the trouble area.

TONE GENERATORS

The tracing procedure will differ according to the type of organ. If electromechanical tone generators are used, the mechanical action is relatively simple to check. If it is working, then any tone failure must be in the electrical part. If the tone generators are mechanical or acoustical with microphone pickups, it is fairly easy to check the microphones when the tone chest is opened. The ones that require more detailed knowledge are the electronic tone generators, which are most prevalent today.

Now which type of organ is it? Does it have separate tone generators for every note, or does it use the lock-oscillator arrangement with 12 master generators? If separate tone generators are used for every note, or even if two or three notes share a tone generator, tracing is relatively simple because only the one note,

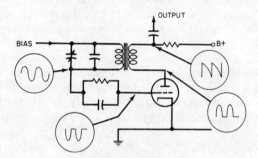

Fig. 9-1. Blocking oscillator using coupling (feedback) transformer.

or a small group, will become inoperative when a generator fails. The main problem may be in locating the generator associated with the dead ones. The best way to do this is to use a circuit continuity tester, with the organ switched off.

In an organ with 12 master oscillators, if one of the master generators goes dead, every note of that name in the instrument will be dead. For example, if the $F\sharp$ oscillator quits, not a single $F\sharp$ in the whole organ will play. If some notes of that name play but others don't, the trouble is either in the key contacts or frequency dividers.

As in other electronic equipment, intermittent faults can usually be traced to bad contacts, either in the keys or in tube or transistor sockets. The same circuit-tracing methods will reveal the faulty contact.

For diagnosing the fault after it has been traced to a specific circuit, an oscilloscope (to observe waveforms) is as essential as a voltmeter (to check working voltages). Most organ oscillator

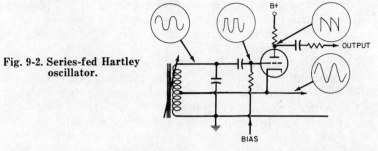

Fig. 9-2. Series-fed Hartley oscillator.

circuits are of the relaxation type, because they give a sawtooth waveform or an approximation of one. But the circuit configuration may look like a conventional Hartley or other type of oscillator. What makes it a relaxation oscillator is the choice of values, or feedback ratio, that makes the circuit oscillate very hard so as to produce many harmonics.

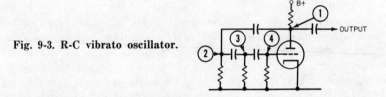

Fig. 9-3. R-C vibrato oscillator.

An oscillator designed to oscillate hard should oscillate even when something is a little wrong. Failure to oscillate indicates some quite obvious defect, such as a completely open- or short-circuited component. Degrees of leakage or change in value may occur without preventing oscillation, but may detune the tone. The waveforms associated with typical circuits (Figs. 9-1, 9-2, 9-4) will aid in tracing the trouble.

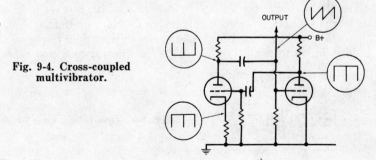

Fig. 9-4. Cross-coupled multivibrator.

115

Some circuits use coils or transformers in either the plate or cathode circuit (Figs. 9-1 and 9-2) and are tuned by capacitors to the correct frequency. Correct tuning (pitch) is achieved by using a variable capacitor or an adjustable core in the coil.

Other circuits are entirely resistive-capacitive. They may work as a phase-shift oscillator (Fig. 9-3) or multivibrator (Fig. 9-4). Multivibrator circuits are not popular for organ use, because each circuit requires two tubes or transistors. Because of the total number of oscillators required, a circuit that requires only one tube or transistor is preferred.

A final form does not use any amplifying element such as tube or transistor, but simple neon tubes that discharge a capacitor at a regular rate to produce the note (Fig. 9-5). Neon-tube circuits can be quite reliable. The illustration shows a circuit of four dividers. Tube (1) fires once for every two cycles of signal from the master oscillator. Tubes (2) and (3) fire once for two firings of tube (1); tubes (4) and (5) fire once each time tube (3) fires twice; and in this manner any number of additional sections may be used.

In each kind of oscillator circuit, defective operation can be investigated by measuring the voltages at various points and looking at the waveform to see whether oscillation is occuring correctly or not. Where oscillation does not occur and the tube or transistor is not defective, it may be worth trying to "shock" the oscillator in operation while watching an oscilloscope. If the key switches the supply voltage, see what happens each time the key is pressed. If the oscillator is the type that runs all the time, break the B+ supply connection and then connect it again while watching the scope. If the oscillator appears to start momentarily and die away quickly, some component in the circuit is either defective or seriously off-value. In oscillators utilizing transformers or coils, a winding may develop short-circuited turns. This will result in no oscillation, even though all voltages are correct.

Frequency Dividers

Divider circuits are similar to master oscillators except that they are pulsed by the next oscillator (or divider) up in frequency (an octave higher), once every two cycles of the upper frequency. It is common to use a tube oscillator for the masters, and neon

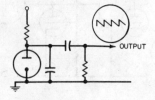

Fig. 9-5. Neon-tube generator.

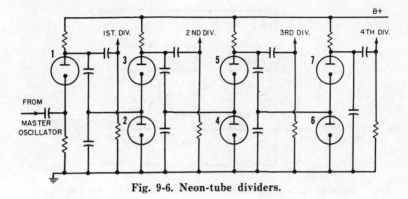

Fig. 9-6. Neon-tube dividers.

oscillators for the dividers (Fig. 9-6) usually arranged so the neons do not oscillate unless the master is running. However, defective values in the neon circuits could either prevent the divider from operating at all, or make it run so fast that it fails to synchronize with the octave above, making the lower note erratic in frequency.

Some divider circuits use tubes in almost identical configuration with the master circuits, merely using synchronization from the higher to the lower frequencies (Fig. 9-7). In checking

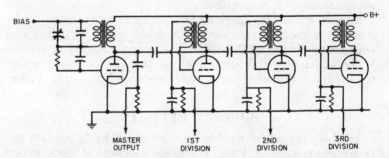

Fig. 9-7. Frequency dividers similar to the master oscillator.

through divider circuits where the lower frequency fails or drifts, use the scope to see whether the upper frequency is reaching it as sync. If the sync is getting through, the fault must be in the values of the lower-frequency circuit. If the sync is not getting through, trace it to where it stops.

For the bistable multivibrator-type divider, the most likely thing is failure of one of the transistors. When both transistors are working, but no signal is received from the octave above, one collector will be at supply voltage and the other at the common emitter voltage, which may be used for coupling (Fig. 9-8).

117

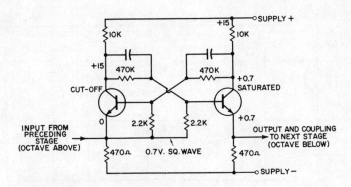

Fig. 9-8. Voltage readings in a bistable voltage divider circuit.

Momentarily applying a signal which reduces the emitter-to-ground voltage should switch the bistable unit to its other condition (collector voltages will change places).

If one transistor becomes shorted, the other one will be permanently nonconducting. If one becomes an open circuit, the other will be permanently conducting. From this combination of facts, it is obvious that either failure produces the same symptoms, from opposite causes, and thus it will not be possible, without removing the transistors, to tell which of the faults exists, and which transistor is responsible.

Removing them for checking or, if a checker is not handy, substituting them with transistors in other dividers, will prove whether this is the trouble. Interchange one transistor at a time. When exchanging transistors with another circuit also transfers the trouble to the other circuit, you have found the faulty device.

SPECIAL EFFECTS

Another area where trouble may develop is in the vibrato circuitry. Every vibrato circuit, except the mechanical types involving moving parts, uses a vibrato oscillator working at a very low frequency (from two to ten cycles per second). In some organs, this frequency is adjustable; in others, there are one or more fixed settings. It is important not only that a vibrato oscillator should oscillate, but also that it should do so *smoothly*. Such low frequencies seldom approach a perfect sine wave, but they should be smooth (Fig. 9-9). The third waveform shown is the most likely cause of "thumping" or "pumping" when the vibrato is on.

Vibrato

Vibrato is distributed to all tones by a vibrato bus, from which the vibrato is applied to the actual tones. The signal from the vibrato bus, in one organ, is applied to a diode in each oscillator circuit. These diodes are in series with capacitors and both are effectively across the tuned circuit (Fig. 9-10). When the diodes are conducting, the extra capacity changes the frequency; when they are cut off, the frequency returns to normal. In this way the output frequency is varied at the vibrato rate.

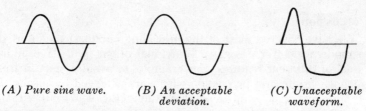

(A) Pure sine wave.   (B) An acceptable   (C) Unacceptable
                            deviation.   waveform.

Fig. 9-9. Waveforms associated with good vibrato operation.

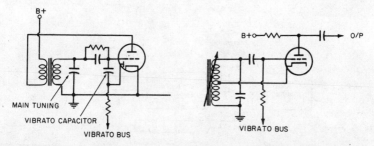

Fig. 9-10. Vibrato system using a di-   Fig. 9-11. Vibrato modulation by
ode and capacitor.   bias variation.

In another method, the vibrato bus voltage is applied to the bias of the oscillator tube or transistor, thus varying the intensity of oscillation. This changes the frequency, too, because of the sawtooth waveform used. As the waveform builds up, the frequency rises, and vice versa (Fig. 9-11).

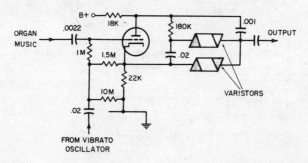

Fig. 9-12. Vibrato modulator stage after tone generator.

119

A third, less often-used method works on the amplifier rather than the tone generators. Here the phase of the amplified signal is fluctuated by changing a resistance value in a phase-shifting network. One vibrator modulator circuit (Fig. 9-12) can thus produce a vibrato effect on the whole organ output or on the output from just one manual; a "bus" to the individual keys is unnecessary.

Percussion

We have covered most of the prevailing circuit elements used in modern electronic organs. Individual organs will have additional or different features. For example, to avoid a shift in frequency, sustain and percussion effects are achieved by means of variable bias, usually on an amplifier stage (Fig. 9-13) rather than by using an oscillator. Incorrect bias, or incorrect range over which the bias voltage swings, can result in tones that die away

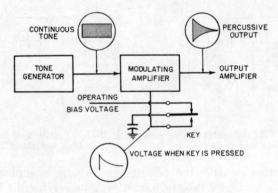

Fig. 9-13. Percussion amplifier method.

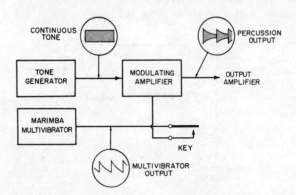

Fig. 9-14. Arrangement for repetitive percussion.

too quickly, too slowly, or never die away completely at all. This is usually adjustable and, if so, can be readily corrected.

Xylophone or marimba effects use a low-frequency multivibrator that brings a sawtooth fluctuating voltage into the key circuit, to simulate the effect of repetitively striking the keys while they are being held down (Fig. 9-14). Failure of this effect could be in the multivibrator, or in the switching that brings its output into the key circuits.

Chimes and other effects synthesize the required sound by mixing various tone components together for the desired effect. If these do not function correctly, very careful checking is needed, to make sure the electronic circuitry provides correct mixing according to the organ's "recipe" for the effect.

Because of their simplicity, formant circuits usually give little trouble. Amplifiers can generate the same troubles common to amplifiers for any other use; so no further discussion is needed here. Loose pieces in speakers and cabinetry can develop buzzes, just as in hi-fi systems. These are such obvious causes that detailed tracing instructions are not required.

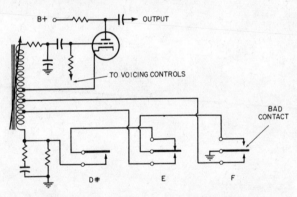

Fig. 9-15. Switching for a shared oscillator.

Contacts

Any electronic organ contains an enormous number of contacts, which may develop troubles. Where two or more notes share the same oscillator circuit, the switching that fixed the frequency of that oscillator is in the key contact (Fig. 9-15) assembly. So, with this kind of organ the trouble may be in the key that sounds bad, or in one nearby. There are contacts on the voice tabs, the special-effects switches, in some cases on the tone controls, and on rhythm bars. In addition to the many switches, there are also several potentiometer controls. These are seldom difficult to locate, and they may be serviced by using the normal control techniques.

A common cause of trouble in organ circuits in the interconnecting leads, of which there are usually quite a few. These use different kinds of terminations (5 pin plug, 7 pin plug, 12 pin plug, and so forth) to make connections virtually foolproof (so you cannot put the wrong plug in the wrong socket). Trouble, in the nature of malfunctioning, can be traced to one or more bad contacts at plug and socket connectors. Clean these thoroughly and improve the contact pressure by whatever means is available.

GLOSSARY

Accompaniment. Also called *great*. On an organ, the lower manual, which provides the musical harmony to the solo.

Action. The term applied to the assembly of key contacts and couplers.

Aeoline. A stop of the string family with high harmonic content.

Attack. The time taken by a tone to build up to its full intensity after a key has been depressed.

Baroque. A type of pipe organ designed to play Baroque music. It lacks expression pedals, vibrato or tremolo, and predominates in the higher pitched mixtures. Some electronic organs include Baroque features, but few electronic Baroque organs have been built as such.

Bass. The lowest frequencies in music. Specifically, the appropriate lowest frequency tone that harmonizes with the chord being played.

Bass Reflex. A speaker enclosure that includes an opening so sound pressures from the rear of the diaphragm can augment the radiation at low frequencies.

Beat. A fluctuation in apparent intensity due to two notes of nearly the same pitch (or frequency) being played at the same time.

Bourdon. A basic bass stop of the flute family of tones.

Brass. General name for tones resembling those from brass instruments (tuba, horn, trumpet, cornet, etc.). It is characterized by a strident quality.

Bus (Bar). A common connection servicing many circuits. It may be connected to keys, either to supply voltage or collect tones; or used for supplying vibrato or other special-effect voltage to control all tones.

Carillon. A bell tower designed to play from a keyboard. In an organ, this may be achieved by tube synthesis of bell-like tones struck with felt hammers or completely electronically.

Celeste. A stop characterized by a slow (about 3 to 4 periods per second) beat. Usually of the diapason family of tones, but in the upper register.

Chimes. A bell-like effect produced by striking tubes or rods with a hammer, or by special tone synthesis electronically.

Chord Coupling. Coupling in which all notes for a specific chord can be played by depressing one button or key.

Chord Organ. An organ with provision for playing a variety of chords, each complete harmony of several notes played at once, by means of a single button or key.

Chorus Effect. Any means of producing the effect of a number of separate voices. Separate oscillators will do this in the bigger organs. Or any means of producing independent voicing, such as applying vibrato to part of the sound, while also reproducing it without vibrato from other parts.

Cipher. A note that plays when it should not.

Clarinet. An organ stop intended to imitate the orchestral instrument. Because of its popularity, most organs include such a stop, though few achieve a good imitation.

Classis Organ. An organ, or ranks of stops, predominating in the diapason family of tones. Little or no vibrato, or a different form, intended to convey a sense of spacious reverberation.

Clavier. The general name for a group of pedals. (The word *manual* is more commonly used for keys played with the hands.)

Counterbass. Also called *contrabass*. A second bass note that will harmonize with a specific chord.

Coupler. Mechanical or electrical coupling enabling more than one note to be played by depressing one key. (*Also see* Octave Coupling, Manual Coupling, *and* Chord Coupling.)

Crescendo. A rapid increase in volume to full orchestra. In organs, a pedal or action that rapidly brings all stops into play, or all those that build power with harmony.

Decay. The time taken for a tone to die away after the stimulus has been removed. This may apply to normal key operation, to the sustain effect, or to percussion operation.

Diapason. The tone quality normally associated with, and characteristic of, pipe organs rather than imitation of some other instrument.

Divider. An electronic circuit somewhat similar to an oscillator and designed to divide the frequency of an existing tone by two in order to produce a tone exactly one octave lower.

Dividing Network. A circuit that feeds different parts of the audio spectrum to different speaker units.

Doppler Cabinet. A speaker cabinet in which either the speaker or a baffle board is rotated or moved to change the length of the sound path cyclically and thereby produce a vibrato effect mechanically.

Drawbars. A name sometimes used for stop switches that are pulled out and pushed in, as opposed to the rocking tablet type. In Hammond organs, manually operated slide resistors controlling the harmonic constitution of a tone, used to build up the organist's own "stops."

Expression. Also called *swell*. The foot-operated control that varies volume.

Flat. A black note taking the name of the white note to its right (e.g., the black note to the left of white note *B* is *B* flat). More generally, any note one semitone lower in tone (to the left).

Flute. Applied to the general group of tones, throughout the organ, in which the tone is almost pure *fundamental*.

Formant. An electrical circuit, the purpose of which is to alter the tone quality of sound amplified by it. A formant filter is applied to the entire output from a manual, rather than to individual tones.

Frequency. The number of vibrations per second that correspond to a particular note. Frequency is the electrical or physical quantity corresponding to pitch in music.

Fundamental. The lowest frequency of a group produced as a single note or tone, and to which all the others are related by being simply numerical multiples, or harmonics.

Generator. The name given to any tone source, whether electromechanical or electronic, and whether a simple type (e.g., oscillator) or more complex (e.g., master oscillator and dividers).

Glide (Glissando). A feature enabling the tone to be shifted by a fraction at a time, either up or down, to effect a continuous change in pitch.

Glockenspiel. A mechanical imitation of bells used in orchestras, also called *Orchestra Bells*.

Great. Traditional organ name for the lower, or accompaniment manual.

Harmonic. One of many tones related to the fundamental in a composite tone (e.g., the third harmonic has a frequency of three times that of the fundamental). (*Also see* Overtone.)

Harmony. A group of notes played simultaneously, to provide the musical supporting effect for the melody.

Interval. The musical difference in pitch between two tones.

Keyswitch. The switch which is operated by the key mechanism to control the tone.

Kinura. A stop of the reed family, having very little fundamental and rich in harmonics. It was introduced in theater organs to add brilliance and is still so used.

Manual. A clavier of keys to be played with the hands. In a two-manual organ, the upper is called the solo, or swell; and the lower the accompaniment, or great.

Manual Coupling. Coupling which causes the same note to sound on another manual when a key is depressed.

Master Oscillator. An electronic tone generator working at a frequency corresponding to a note in the top octave of the organ's range. Lower notes are obtained from it by dividers, octave by octave.

Melodia. A stop of the flute family, useful for solo.

Melody. The tune of a musical piece, usually played one note at a time, on the swell or solo manual.

Multivibrator. A circuit that characteristically produces a square-wave or sawtooth output. It can be used as a tone generator or a frequency divider, according to precise circuit configuration and choice of values.

Note. The sound produced from one key; a single tone, consisting of the fundamental with whatever harmonics or overtones make up the appropriate composite tone quality.

Octave. The interval of pitch corresponding to frequencies, one of which is exactly twice the other. In the accepted musical scale, an octave is divided into twelve *semitones.*

Octave Coupling. Coupling in which a note is sounded one octave higher or lower when a key is depressed.

Oscillator. Any form of electronic tone generator.

Overtone. Any one of the related tones that add to a fundamental to give tone quality. Overtones are numbered *from* the fundamental; so the second harmonic becomes the first overtone, etc.

Pedal. *See* Clavier.

Percussion. Musical sounds characterized by sharp attack and varying decay, rather than steady tones. Organ percussion is achieved by having the tone start to decay the instant it is played, without waiting until the key is released.

Piston. A push-button switch, either under manuals, which activate groups of stops by means of relays, or for toe operation, in which case the action is only sustained while pressed, such as for cymbals, or sforzando.

Pizzicato. A rapid, plucked effect, similar to that when a violin is played by plucking.

Pitch. The musical quality of sounds that depends on their (fundamental) frequency.

Quality. A way of describing the harmonic content of tones, corresponding to the musical characteristic known as timbre.

Reed. A tone group characterized by richness in overtones, or harmonics. The opposite of the flute group.

Register. A range of notes used for playing a particular piece or part of it (e.g., melody or harmony), particularly the range covered by a clavier or manual.

Reverberation. An effect that simulates the spaciousness of a large building. It is achieved by artificially adding a short time echo effect.

Romantic Organ. One of a type with provision for imitating orchestral and other sounds. Largely superseded by **Theater Organ.**

Rhythm Bar. A bar used in some organs to enable rhythmic playing of a chord, or group of notes, without interrupting the pressure on the notes or chord button.

Scale. A succession of notes, of which the eight white notes from *C* to *C* an octave higher are one example (*C, D, E, F, G, A, B, C*), from which the major notes in a musical piece are always selected.

Semitone. The interval between each note and the one next to it, black or white. Twelve intervals make up an octave.

Sforzando. Similar to Crescendo, except that an organ with both puts in all stops, harmonious and discordant, with sforzando.

Sharp. Symbolized by ♯. A black note taking the name of the white note to its left (e.g., the black note to the right of white note *F* is F sharp). More generally, any note one semitone higher (to the right).

Solo. 1. A single voice or instrument, playing a melody. 2. Also called swell. The upper manual on the organ.

Stop. A tablet or drawbar-operated switch or selector that yields a desired tone quality or part of it.

String. A tone group that imitates the quality of stringed instruments—rich in harmonics, but not strident as brass nor thin as reeds.

Sustain. A feature that allows the sound from a note to decay slowly after the key is released.

Swell. Also called solo. The traditional name for the upper manual.

Tablet. A stop or selector switch operated by a rocking bar or panel.

Tibia. A family of notes similar to flute, but characteristic of organs, rather than imitative of orchestral instruments.

Timbre. Also called tone color. The musical name describing the overtone structure of a tone.

Tone Color. Electronic term corresponding to timbre.

Transistor. A relatively new electronic device that replaces the better-known tubes, with considerable economy in space, heat generation, and efficiency.

Tremolo. A warbling or fluctuating effect to the tone of an instrument, characterized by variation in intensity rather than pitch. (*Also see* Vibrato.)

Vibrato. An effect similar to tremolo but characterized by fluctuation in pitch rather than intensity.

Voice. A general name for the sounding of an organ note or notes with a particular tone color or quality.

INDEX